D0464073

A PUBLICATION FROM THE JAMES FORD BELL COLLECTION
IN THE UNIVERSITY OF MINNESOTA LIBRARY

carta marina

WORLD GEOGRAPHY IN STRASSBURG, 1525

by HILDEGARD BINDER JOHNSON

UNIVERSITY OF MINNESOTA PRESS · MINNEAPOLIS

The portrait of Lorenz Fries on the title page is used by permission
of the Bibliothèque Nationale in Paris, and the reproduction of the
Carta Marina of 1525 contained in the pocket of this book by
permission of the Staatsbibliothek of Munich

TO

Palmer O. Johnson

TEACHER, SCHOLAR, STATISTICIAN

September 13, 1891–January 24, 1960

OURTESIES and dedications — such as were customary among authors, printers, publishers, and patrons, and printed with much embellishment in books and on maps of the period represented by the *Carta Marina* — would outrun the space allotted to a preface in our time. Nor is it feasible to list by name every friend and scholar to whom I am indebted for helpful suggestions and critical comments at various stages of this study, which has to be concerned with Ptolemy, historical cartography, the arts of printing and woodcutting, and cultural history, in order to attain the proper perspective for an evaluation of the first German wall map of the world and the guidebook which was printed with it. The hope which the outstanding German historian of medicine, Carl Sudhoff, expressed in 1902 that the *Carta Marina* by Lorenz Fries would receive more than passing notice could not have been fulfilled more than sixty years later without the opportunity of communicating with scholars in the United States and in Europe.

My thanks go first to an institution and its staff: the rare books from the age of discovery in the James Ford Bell Collection, and the general resources of the Walter Library at the University of Minnesota, made the broad approach of my study possible, and many of my problems could not have been solved without the unfailing assistance of the staff of the Library.

Thanks are also due to Macalester College: President Harvey M. Rice arranged for a reduced teaching load in 1962 and I was granted a sabbatical leave from 1962 to 1963; the Macalester Faculty Research and Travel Fund contributed to the expenses of travel to Munich in 1960; and the Weyerhaeuser Library staff of Macalester College rendered many practical services during the whole period of writing.

Among friends abroad who helped to overcome various difficulties, I must mention by name Dr. Emil Meynen, Director of the Institut für Landeskunde at the Bundesanstalt in Godesberg; Dr. Ruth Ewert of Munich and Rottach/Tegernsee; Dr. Gerhard Oestreich of the Universität of Hamburg, formerly of the Freie Universität Berlin; and Dr. Joachim Lachman, Director of the Landesarchiv, Berlin.

I extend special thanks to Dr. Alois Fauser and Dr. Edeltraut Seifert of the Staatsbibliothek at Munich for valuable suggestions during my inspection of the original *Carta Marina* in July 1960. Dr. Fauser kindly supervised the technical work of photographing the map in 1961. The reader will find the reproduction in the pocket of this book necessary for the perusal of the fourth chapter and helpful in the reading of the fifth.

Mrs. Mary Nakasone prepared a map of Strassburg and the Upper Rhine Valley (page 6) to help the reader with frequently mentioned place names.

HILDEGARD BINDER JOHNSON

Minneapolis
July 1963

STRASSBURG IN 1525

RGENTINA (Strassburg) is a capital on the Rhine in Alsace in a plain between two mountain ranges where four navigable rivers join, the Rhine, Bruche, Ill, and Kinzig. Across the Rhine is a long wooden bridge, which is kept up at great expense. A wide beautiful open space between the bridge and the city is so guarded by strong watchtowers and moats that it is almost impossible to reach the city except by the legal road. Further protection is given by moats at each gate and by bulwarks, strong towers, and masterfully built lookouts and fortifications. This city was named after a silver mine, but after it was destroyed by Attila and its walls torn down to open all its streets, it was called the town of streets . . . I believe the name comes from the fact that the city is a thoroughfare between Lotharingia, France, Burgundy, Lombardy, Switzerland, Breisgau, Swabia, the Netherlands . . .

Thus did Lorenz Fries, who styled himself doctor of medicine, astrologer, and cosmographer on the title page of another book, describe Strassburg in his *Guide and Instructions for the Carta Marina, on which one can see where one is in the world and where every sea, country and city is,* published by Johannes Grüninger together with twelve sheets for a large wall map, in Strassburg in 1525, 1527, and 1530.[1] Fries lived in the city only from 1519 to 1525, during which time he formed a close friendship with Grüninger, who like him was not a native of Strassburg, but worked there for half a century as one of the city's many great printers in the era of humanistic glory and Reformation.[2]

[3]

This was the period when traditional knowledge about the earth was becoming interwoven with as yet fragmentary news about lands freshly discovered, when Ptolemy's geography was revived and at the same time recognized as inadequate, when the established church was attacked from within by the Reformation and from without by Islam, when humanists hoped to re-establish standards of classical knowledge and scientists pioneered with observations and measurements of natural phenomena. It was most of all a period of tension between adherence to recognized authority and revolutionary resistance against it.

This process of revising accepted views is at work at all times but it was accelerated during the Renaissance — a historical circumstance that gives interest even to our interpretation of a modest book and a poorly executed map of the world. Stories about long voyages and about lands and peoples whose existence had been entirely unsuspected were both fascinating and frightening to the burghers along the Upper Rhine valley at the beginning of the sixteenth century. The way in which the *Carta Marina* and *Uslegung* presented the beginning of a new world view to the general public of Strassburg in 1525 is of particular interest in our time, when man once more must reorient his thinking about space.

Old maps are part of cultural history. They were created by cartographers, scholars, explorers, and printers who did not live isolated from their environment and whose works are never without antecedents nor exempt from the incidents which affect the growth of geographic knowledge. Thus Fries's book and map cannot be appraised without first considering the peculiar circumstances that led to their publication. Some information about Strassburg, Fries, and Grüninger is necessary to give us an understanding not only of the background of these publications but also of the role that author and publisher played in communicating a new view of the world to German readers.

Strassburg was the largest and the greatest center of learning among the imperial free cities who were joined in the League of Ten Cities in the valley of the Upper Rhine, and the end of the fifteenth and the first half of the sixteenth century make up the greatest period in its history. The city excelled in the science of municipal government and in the art of printing, and, fittingly, erected a monument to Gutenberg on the square before its venerable city hall.

The tower of Strassburg's cathedral of *unserer lieben Frauen Werck*, with its unique glow that emanates from the handhewn red Vosges sandstone of which it was built, was then as now the symbol of the capital of Alsace. This is one gothic steeple whose architect, Erwin von Steinbach, we know. Begun in 1015, it was not until 1439 that the single spire of the edifice soared to 438 feet and a grand rose window over the west portal greeted the worshipers. And on the steps of this cathedral Master Grüninger had one of his bookstalls.[3]

Fries was geographically correct in stressing Strassburg's location at the crossroads of water and land routes from Marseille and Lyon to Basel, then via the Rhine to Frankfurt, Cologne, and Holland, and also to Nancy and Paris by branching off near Strassburg via the "stairways" of Zabern at the northern end of the Vosges Mountains.[4] From the east, Strassburg could be reached over its famous five-hundred-yard wooden bridge, whose pontoons and piles were probably made from trees of the Black Forest, the logs rafted down the Kinzig as Sebastian Münster reported in his *Cosmographia* of 1544. Fries describes the only other bridge on the Upper Rhine, at Basel, as "a beautiful bridge made of stone, such as one finds few in this world."[5] Strassburg, located importantly at the junction of Rhine and Ill, the latter navigable from Colmar to its mouth, had been served by a ferry for centuries until a first pontoon bridge was built in 1333. In 1388, when the city needed faster transportation for troops and military supplies, a new, second bridge was constructed further downstream near the Robertsau, "the wide and beautiful open space" which had impressed Fries. Strass-

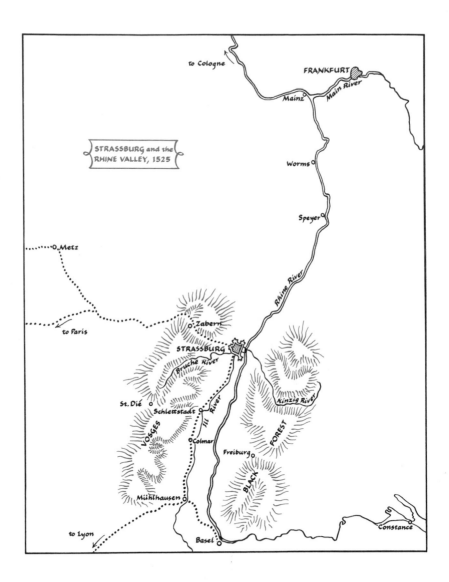

to Cologne

FRANKFURT

Mainz   Main River

Worms

Speyer

o Metz

to Paris

Rhine River

STRASSBURG and the
RHINE VALLEY, 1525

Zabern

STRASSBURG

Bruche River

Kinzig River

St. Dié

Schlettstadt

Ill River

VOSGES

Colmar

BLACK FOREST

Freiburg

Mühlhausen

to Lyon

Basel

Constance

burg's imperial right to build this bridge also implied the duty of repair, because the emperor recognized "its great utility for the country and Empire." It was no less useful for Strassburg's merchants and visitors than it was for the emperor, and boatmen from Strassburg are reported to have ventured as far as Cologne and even Holland.

Strassburg was most of all a river port, as it still is. Gradually the city was able to gain the exclusive right for navigation to and from Mainz, exacting a toll from boats passing under its bridge. Thus the city not only reigned supreme on the Upper Rhine, but derived some profit from navigation on the middle stretch of the Rhine. The city's printers could ship the sheets of unbound books to the Easter and fall fairs at Frankfurt directly by water from the wharves on the Ill to those on the Main. Grüninger often hurried to ready books to be packed in barrels which his men would roll onto the carts to go to the quay of St. Jean. To be able to ship heavy loads from Strassburg to Frankfurt on the sturdy river craft was an advantage not enjoyed by printers in Nürnberg, where humanism and mathematical geography flourished and where the great publishing house of Koberger tried using cumbersome and expensive leather bags to protect the pages from the rain as they traveled overland by wagon. Fries understood what Frankfurt meant to Strassburg merchants: "It is a port and trade city for all of Germany. Twice a year, in March and in September, more merchants than one can count come here from all over the world, from Holland and Hungary, Bohemia, France, and Italy. Really, it is unimaginable." [6]

The Rhine flooded in years of heavy precipitation; Münster tells us that the summer rains of 1480 damaged every mill between Strassburg and Basel. The Ill, less subject to flooding, served Upper and Lower Alsace as a waterway parallel to the Rhine, carrying the water of all the tributaries from the eastern slopes of the Vosges to the city; inside Strassburg the Ill is called Bruche, or Breusch, the name of its last major tributary. Through the centuries an intricate system of canals, moats, waterways, and quays had been built around the core and first site of Strassburg on an island in the Ill.

The maintenance of the canals was an unending chore. During the first half of the sixteenth century, moats and canals were included in the rebuilding of the fortification system which finally amounted to a three-line defense that saved Strassburg even through the Thirty Years' War. Walls and ditches were replaced, as well as many high square towers that were too vulnerable after gunpowder came into use. The first to be rebuilt, in 1508 and 1511, was the round bulwark by the Kronenburger Gate to the northwest. The northernmost points, the Roseneck and Steinstrasser Thor, were renewed in 1510. The moat along the wall which guarded the city toward the floodplain of the Rhine to the east was widened during the drought of 1516. After that a new tower was erected on the same site between Steintor and Judentor behind the Wasser-Supp Gasse (water-soup alley, one of the many street names which mirrors the common aspects of life in Strassburg around the turn of the sixteenth century). In 1524, more ramparts were repaired around the Weissenburgthor. A year later the convent of St. Clair was razed so that a tower surrounded by water could be erected on the same site; here the large warehouses, some of them seven stories high, were also built. Some newly erected rampart of 1525 near another lookout tower is reported to have been torn down to be replaced by a new and better one in 1568. How the burghers felt about this urban renewal project may be gathered from an inscription put on the New Gate of 1530: *Wo aber der Herr die Stadt nit behüt, so wacht umsonst der Wächter anno MCXXX mense Octobri* (The guard is on watch in vain when God does not protect the city).

The name of a bulwark erected in 1529 near St. Nicholas reflects the fear which gripped Christian citizens of the Holy Roman Empire of the German Nation everywhere in the late twenties of the sixteenth century: Türkischer Wall (Turkish Rampart). Sultan Soliman had overrun Hungary and reached Vienna on September 26, 1529, to besiege that city for three weeks. Vienna was saved, mainly through possession of superior artillery, an armament which Strassburg did not neglect. As early as 1474 one of its heavy cannons is recorded as being drawn by eighteen horses, and artillery was in place on the ramparts most of the time, even on peaceful-sounding occasions.

One such occasion when the city's remarkable talent for precautionary measures was demonstrated is recorded by Dr. Sebastian Brant, the famous author of the *Ship of Fools* and secretary of his native city after 1500; this was the grand entrance of the new Bishop, Count William of Honstein, on October 4, 1507, when Emperor Maximilian paid Strassburg one of twenty visits he made during his reign, more than any other monarch before or after. The city swarmed with people. The arrangements for which Dr. Brant meticulously recorded expenses included a double row of armed citizens, marching along a train of six hundred forty horses ridden by prelates, margraves, counts, and barons and their retinue from the city gates to the Bishop's Palace. The cannons were ready for action on the ramparts; the members of the guilds, Grüninger probably among them, had been spotted throughout the city to watch for fire resulting from arson or carelessness. Several hundred peasants from the bailiwicks adjoining the city had been instructed in helping to maintain order. This was the last procession accorded a Roman Catholic prelate until the occupation of Strassburg by France in 1681, and no unhappy incident is recorded in connection with the event.

During 1525 Strassburg's fortifications helped to protect it from one of the worst scourges that has ever befallen the Upper Rhine valley — the Peasants' War. Strassburg's sympathies with Lutheranism were already well known when the rebelling peasants of Molsheim, a Strassburg bailiwick, swore on May 4, 1525, that they wanted "to assist God's word, the holy scriptures and justice," in the same evangelistic spirit that had animated the Upper Alsatian peasant rebellion. After the battle of Zabern, Strassburg showed clemency toward the insurgents in its bailiwicks; there were no executions, imprisonment, or tortures, but only fairly mild collective fines.[7]

The city's flourishing economy, its sheltering walls, and its benevolence attracted artisans, craftsmen, and merchants — the well-to-do and also the destitute: the countryside and roads were unsafe in the twenties because of marauding deserters, homeless folk, and fugitives from the law. In spite of wars and epidemics (the plague of 1449 is said to have killed sixteen thousand people in Strassburg) Strassburg's population increased by an eighth (about four thousand people) between 1460 and 1560, and by 1525 twenty to thirty thousand people might well have been crowded inside the walls during the day in an area of approximately five hundred acres.[8]

While men like Grüninger and Fries were welcomed as citizens, Jews were banned from the city after the middle of the fourteenth century, when a mysterious epidemic was blamed on their alleged poisoning of the wells and nine hundred Jewish people were burned in a street named Brandgasse. Jews had to enter Strassburg daily through the Judentor and were warned by two trumpet signals from the cathedral to leave at nightfall. Gardeners, peasants, butchers, and peddlers also came in from the villages and former manors that had been added between 1351 and 1507 to the city's territory.[9] In picturing the crowds bustling along the narrow winding streets we must imagine churchmen, high officials, and city employees on their way to work in convents, the cathedral, the venerable town hall or Pfaltz, the new mint opposite it, the treasury or Pfennigthurm, and the toll house. Craftsmen were going to their Stuben, the meeting places of the guilds; men and women crowded around the stalls on the steps of the cathedral or before a printed illustrated announcement at its portal; others were looking at the displays in the open arcades; journeymen drove the sturdy horses that drew covered wagons making deliveries to the city's massive five-story granaries; dusty travelers on horseback, with messages and samples in their satchels, sought out addresses among the nearly three hundred winding alleys and streets; halberdiers passed on their way to a watchtower; gangs of the poor worked on the ramparts in return for shelter and food at the Elenden Herberge, the hostel for indigent travelers; figures in simple garb took medicines to the hospitals or the sick house on an isle outside the western wall where syphilis cases were quarantined by 1520.[10] Though we do not know which street Fries lived in, he certainly often went to the shops to buy paper, an astrolabe, a compass, or a ruler; to a pharmacy to get the foreign herbs and spices which aroused his interest in faraway lands; or to Grüninger's office on the Sand Quaie or in the Schlauchgasse.[11]

The noise and dust from razing, building, and digging must have been a constant accompaniment of the crowded existence of Strassburgers in the third decade of the sixteenth century. Scenes from every part of their daily lives — from intimacies between lovers and domestic activities to the public spectacles of executions, religious processions, and royal receptions — vividly portrayed in contemporary woodcuts,[12] are very helpful in a comparative evaluation of illustrations in the *Uslegung* and the *Carta Marina*.

Strassburg's pride was its government by checks and balances constitutionalized in the Schwörbrief of 1482, which marks the beginning of the city's greatest political power.[13] The city also was conscious of the heritage of Gutenberg, who lived there from 1434 to the middle forties, when he went to Mainz, and proud of the work of its famous printers at the end of the fifteenth and beginning of the sixteenth century, including Mentelin, Flach, Knoblochzer, Hupfuff, Schott, Kunast, and Grüninger. The last printed many books by the best-known personalities of Strassburg's intellectual and spiritual life of his time. Geiler von Kaysersberg, the theologian, had come from Freiburg; Jacob

Wimpheling, the historian, scholar, and educator from Schlettstadt, was the friend of the greatest humanists north of the Alps; and Sebastian Brant, a native and the most colorful of all Strassburgers, had returned from the university of Basel. He established with his *Narrenschiff* a type of satire which became the characteristic Strassburgian humor. A second representative of this literary style was the restless Thomas Murner, whose *Narrenbeschwörung* of 1512 was inspired by Brant and of whom we shall hear more later. John Fischart, who published during the second half of the sixteenth century, was the third to follow in Strassburg's tradition of ridiculing human foibles. The city's leadership in classical secondary education, under the humanist Johann Sturm who opened the famous gymnasium in 1538, had its root in the general humanistic climate of the city.

The Reformation came quickly and with certainty in Strassburg. Forerunners were Meister Eckhardt, a native of the city, who was accused of heresy; Johann Tauler, a student of Eckhardt whose mystical prose inspired Luther; and Johann Geiler von Kaysersberg, the greatest preacher the cathedral ever had, who demanded peaceful reforms, although he never considered breaking away from the church during the thirty-four years he preached. Many Strassburgers bought his sermons and liked them best richly illustrated — the way Grüninger turned them out.

By 1518 Luther's ninety-five theses had been affixed to several churches, and his sermons were in print. Matthäus Zell, who came to the cathedral in 1518, preached outright Lutheranism from a movable platform which the carpenter's guild had made for him after the Grand Chapter of the cathedral forbade him to preach his heresies from the pulpit hallowed by Geiler. By 1523, Wolfgang Capito of Hagenau, Martin Bucer of Schlettstadt, and Casper Hedio of Ettlingen across the Rhine had gathered in Strassburg and preached in the evangelical manner. On December 1, 1523, the magistrate ordered that ministers were to preach the gospel — a rule that supported the adherents of Luther. And on September 29, 1524, he ruled that alms from monasteries and convents were to go into a common treasury to be administered by the city. By the end of 1524, mass was said in German, and in 1525, only four masses in the cathedral and one mass in the other churches were permitted daily. Clergymen had to become citizens of the city after a decree of January 26, 1525. Total abolition of the mass was demanded on various occasions by the people during the next three years, and in 1529 the magistrate gave in to the vote of the Assembly of Three Hundred — with one single dissent — to "discontinue mass until it was proved that it was a work agreeable to the Lord." [14] The secularization of thirteen convents and monasteries proceeded rather amiably and was completed by 1530.

One can agree with the French historian who writes that the Reformation was not merely decreed but was a reality in Strassburg by the end of 1525, supported by all of the great printers with one exception. [15] Johannes Grüninger, seeing "that many others made preparations to move" wrote to Hans Koberger, his business partner in Nürnberg, on Sunday, August 13, 1524, that he "had ordered quarters at the bishop's at Zabern in order to print there for a while." [16]

JOHANNES GRÜNINGER

STEEMED and affable Grüninger: when you asked me some time ago to do the world map for everybody's quicker and clearer understanding in smaller size that it was before, I did not want to disappoint you because of our long-standing friendship.[1]

This dedication by "Lorenz Fries, natural philosopher, to the honorable Johann Grieninger, citizen and bookprinter at Strassburg" is one of the bits of information from which Grüninger's life and his part in publishing the *Carta Marina* and the *Uslegung* must be pieced together.[2] The variation in the spelling of his name is characteristic of the period.[3]

Grüninger was born in Mark-gröningen, Swabia, son of Reinhart, probably around 1460.[4] He was already a master of the printer's trade when he came to Basel in 1480, and since his last publication was dated 1531, it is no exaggeration to say that he was an active printer for half a century, a period that coincided with the highest point in Strassburg's illustrious intellectual history. He bought his citizen's right in Strassburg on October 2, 1482, and became a member of the goldsmiths' guild, Zur Steltz, named for its emblem of crossed stilts, after November 15, 1502.[5] This guild included all respectable printers, that is, those who maintained "genuine printing establishments," but not the "common printers, formcutters, bookbinders, and painters of playing cards," who could only take part in the guild's activities but not be voting members.[6] We shall see later that Grüninger was particularly sensitive to the reproach by a Nürnberg scholar that the illustrations on his maps looked like pictures on playing cards.

Three periods are discernible in Grüninger's life as a printer as it was connected with events in Strassburg and associated with different authors — 1484–1502, 1503–1517, and 1518–1531.

His first work was Peter Comestor's *Historia Scolastica*, printed in cooperation with Heinrich Ingweiler. After that, he printed many magnificent folio volumes for himself, from the *Margarita Martiniana* of 1484 to the celebrated *Publii Vergilii Maronis Opera* of 1502 which Dr. Sebastian Brant edited for him and which was one of "the finest books" of the period.[7] Among some sixty-one books printed during these eighteen years, thirty-two were in folio, seventeen in quarto, and twelve in octavo size.[8]

About the turn of the century, Grüninger printed editions of classic books for scholars and works by contemporary scholars, among them Reisch's *Margarita Philosophica*, which he reprinted in 1504 from Johann Schott's edition. He also issued Sebastian Brant's *Narrenschiff* in 1494, immediately after its first publication in Basel; Jacob Wimpheling's *Slettstattensis Elegantiarum* in 1498; and surgical books in German by Hieronymus Brunschwig in 1497 and 1500, which were reprinted later.

Since he knew no Latin, he could not read most of the books he printed during the first period and was dependent on good correctors, who, after 1500, he had in Johannes Adelphus, Gervasius Sopher, and Matthias Ringmann. These proofreaders were under pressure to get their work done speedily so that Grüninger, increasingly more market- than product-conscious, could get new editions ready for the fairs at Frankfurt.[9] The close integration of editing, illustrating, and writing which produced the magnificent volumes of the *Ship of Fools* (1494), Terence (1496), Horace (1498), Boetius (1501), and Vergil (1502), no longer characterizes the second period.

Since authors received no royalties, publishers faced a problem in getting high-quality manuscripts — good copies of classical authors or original writings by contemporaries. Grüninger was unlike Aldus Manutius of Venice, Hans Koberger of Nürnberg, or Johannes Froben of Basel, who were friends of great humanists and scholars themselves and took much pride in producing books in Latin, Greek, and Hebrew. Though Grüninger knew Sebastian Brant, Jacob Wimpheling, and Hieronymus Gebwiler, all distinguished members of the Sodalitas Litteraria at Strassburg, there is no indication that he fraternized much with the members of this literary society, in which Strassburg took pride as did other cities where humanism flourished.[10] At the beginning of the sixteenth century, the public was not at all illiterate in cities like Strassburg with their convents, churches, and city schools, reading masters, and women who taught reading — simple enough, but still reading. The lay reader wanted books and was willing to pay for them, but they had to be in German. Grüninger published more and more German books during the second decade of the sixteenth century and also issued German translations of his Latin publications, sometimes almost simultaneously; but his greatest successes were his richly illustrated volumes, and he continued to go to considerable expense to get good designs for his woodcutters and good craftsmen to prepare the blocks.[11]

In a large workshop such as Grüninger maintained, it is not possible to draw a sharp line between designers and woodcutters. Among the great artists who drew designs — pictures, borders, title-page illustrations, illuminated letters — for Grüninger's shop were Erhard Schlitzoe, Hans Wechtlin, Hans Baldung Grien, Strassburg's most famous artist of the Renaissance, and Hans Franck, perhaps the most representative woodcut designer of the Alsatian school of illustrators. Many of Grüninger's illustrations have not been identified as the work of any particular artist but simply as originating in his workshop. This was enough: his name stood for a style.[12]

He collected an increasing number of wood blocks which were used many times, often without relation to the contents of the book; but these adornments were the delight of contemporaries and still are, for the student of cultural history. He rarely let other printers use his blocks and only seven were found in other printers' publications by Paul Kristeller, the thorough investigator of woodcut illustrations of the period. Other printers were much more lenient in this regard.[13] In fact, Grüninger appears to have employed woodcutters for his own press in his own house, which became intolerable under complicated guild rules. Printing and woodcutting, the first originally related to the goldsmiths', the second to the carpenters' trade, were governed by different guilds, and no master of one trade could control masters or members of another. Grüninger still represents the earlier practice of close relation between printer and woodcutter.[14]

In addition to becoming known as the printer of "merry books" in German among lay readers, and of carelessly done books among scholars, Grüninger also drew attention to the copyright problem as early as 1502. By 1514, a General Superintendent of the Presses in the Holy Roman Empire in the person of Jacob Oessler, doctor of law and attorney at the Bishop's court at Strassburg, sold publisher's privileges, among them protection against reprinting. Grüninger was one of the first to buy such a privilege. Some of his books, and the *Carta Marina*, contain warnings against reprinting and unauthorized sale.

During the second period of his career he appears to have discontinued the printing of broadsides, the Einblattdrucke of earlier years; none is found dated later than 1510.[15] These indulgences, almanacs, and prayers with woodcuts and text reflect the styles characteristic of the studio through about twenty years. Though these were discontinued, artists like Hans Franck and Erhard Schlitzoc furnished designs for blocks about five and a half by three and a half inches and Hans Baldung Grien drew a number of designs for Grüninger during the second decade of the new century. Of greatest interest to the student of maps is the work of the formcutters in Grüninger's shop who, by about 1510, perhaps even as early as 1507, began to make a new kind of block, usually larger than before and showing maps rather than pictures. The formcutters cut away on their pearwood along straight rhumb lines and around small circles, scraped with scorpers to shade large areas of oceans, cut Latin and German names which were strung along coastlines, made winding double lines for rivers and weird shapes for mountains which look like strings of beads or fat caterpillars. They cut little figures on thrones and transferred designs of cannibals and animals to fill the open spaces. Master Grüninger was going into the map-publishing business, in which he was a great success, for he printed at least eighty thousand, very likely nearer a hundred thousand, large map sheets, in a little over twenty years. He published from three thousand to three thousand five hundred wall maps composed of separate sheets during the last ten years of his career.[16] All of his wall maps were designed by Martin Waldseemüller or copied from Waldseemüller's originals.

Without question, twelve blocks over 445 by 620 millimeters were, by 1517, standing around the shop and had been being stacked away there for about five years. It is certain that four more blocks for a European map, each block 400 by 575 millimeters did not leave the shop between 1511 and 1527. Since Master Grüninger was not one to throw blocks away even after they had yielded a thousand printed copies, another set, equally large, very likely was around after 1507, but not used again; these were the blocks for Waldseemüller's Ptolemy map.

Waldseemüller's world map of 1507 was a great success. Its publication may well have marked the beginning of Grüninger's friendship with the famous geographer from St. Dié.[17] This friendship is of interest because Fries's *Carta Marina* and *Uslegung* would not have been possible without Grüninger's loyalty to the heritage of Waldseemüller. Waldseemüller's friend, the chaplain of St. Dié, Gauthier Lud, secretary to Duke René of Lorraine who was patron of the gymnasium in St. Dié, published the *Speculi Orbis Succinctiss* through Grüninger's press in 1507.[18] Matthias Ringmann, Waldseemüller's close friend and Grüninger's corrector, had studied with Jacob Wimpheling and was a member of the literary society at St. Dié, but left in 1505, lived in Strassburg during 1505 to 1507, and was in Basel by 1508.

In 1508, Grüninger printed a letter about geometry composed during Strassburg's pre-Lenten carnival by Waldseemüller, who had come "from Gaul to Germany for the Bacchanalia," as he called the carnival. Grüninger worked fast, as usual, to get the book *Margarita Philosophica*, in which the letter appeared, ready for the Frankfurt fair.

In 1509, he printed the fifth edition of Waldseemüller's *Cosmographia Introductio*, famous for its little globe design and its large map, both of which accompanied the 1507 edition and showed the word *America* on land west of the Oceanus occidentalis.[19]

I do not intend here to discuss fully the question of where the large wall map of 1507 was printed.[20] But I can adduce some evidence in support of the view that the Waldseemüller designs were cut and also printed in Strassburg, very likely in Grüninger's shop.

First, we have no reason to believe there was a large woodcutting establishment in St. Dié, and, in Strassburg, only Grüninger's shop produced large wall maps between 1511 and 1527. The wall map of 1507 has a most elaborate border design, typical of Grüninger's productions, strongly suggesting that Waldseemüller took his designs to Strassburg for engraving. Why would Grüninger, who was to be so reluctant to let others use the blocks of his Ptolemy maps of 1522, be willing to let a little press at St. Dié use the largest blocks his shop had produced? It not only took a great woodcutting establishment, it also required a "greater press" and a "new set-up" to make copies of maps twenty-three and a half by seventeen to eighteen inches.[21]

Secondly, twelve sheets this large demanded not only an elaborate workshop for cutting the blocks, but also shipping faculties, which were available at Strassburg and probably lacking in St. Dié. We know that the map was sold fast after it was printed.[22]

Thirdly, the cooperation between Waldseemüller and Grüninger is documented by the fifth edition of the *Cosmographia* and continued with the publication of maps designed by Waldseemüller and Ringmann's guide to them in *Instructio Manuductionem Pretans in Cartem Itinerariam* published in April 1511. These formed another large printing venture of four sheets, 400 by 575 millimeters each, with one map designed by Ringmann and a letter from Ringmann to Waldseemüller. Grüninger also printed an abbreviated German guide to the maps in 1511 and must have saved the blocks, since the map was printed again in 1520 and a smaller-sized *Instructio* was reprinted in 1527 with a new map index added.[23]

Fourthly, an interesting phrase appears in the *Globus Mundi Declaratio sive Descriptio Mundi* of August 31, 1509, and in the German edition of the same book, *Der welt-kugel Beschrybung*, both printed by Grüninger. On March 18, 1509, Grüninger had announced at the end of a German edition of the fourth voyage of Amerigo Vespucci — the same voyage that appeared in Waldseemüller's *Cosmographia Introductio* — that "the reader will find and read in the near future how the globe and the description of the whole world is to be understood." That was on March 18; only three weeks later, on April 8, in *Der welt-kugel Beschrybung*, the reader was told at the end of the last chapter:

If you want to know how far it is from one place to the other you can hardly learn this from the little sphere because of its size which shall therefore not be described or explained here. However, if you desire to learn such, then you must look at our large map and the *speculum orbis*. There you find it really divided according to distance everywhere.[24]

We have here the publisher Grüninger's suggestion in a book he printed that we look at another of his books and at a large map. Grüninger was not the man to aid the sale of an item as expensive as the large wall map of 1507 was unless he had himself had a part in the production of it.

In summary, not only the technical difficulty of cutting but the problem of shipping blocks and marketing prints, Grüninger's well-known unwillingness to loan blocks, the general collaboration between the St. Dié geographers and Grüninger, and the interpretation of a reference to the map from the publisher's point of view increase the near-certainty that the map of 1507 was printed by Grüninger in Strassburg.

Grüninger would never again associate with so distinguished a group of geographers as the three men from St. Dié: Ringmann, Waldseemüller, and Lud. He was probably about sixty in 1518, which marks the third period in his career. Waldseemüller died in 1518, Fries published his first book with Grüninger in 1518, the last wood blocks for Waldseemüller's *Carta Marina* were prepared around 1516, and Fries arrived in Strassburg in 1519. We can say that Grüninger's third period started with the Reformation in Strassburg, which affected the lives of both Fries and Grüninger, and deepened the "long-standing friendship" between them.

Between 1517 and 1531, the year of the last known publication by Grüninger and the probable year of his death, Schmidt records one hundred titles published by Grüninger, to which we add one by Fries found later. Seventeen books deal with medicine, alchemy, or astrology and include new editions of old favorites, for instance Hieronymus Brunschwig's *Das Buch zu distillieren*. Not included in these seventeen are the medical books by Fries, who was the author of sixteen of Grüninger's publications during this period.

By far the greatest number of his more than one hundred publications were anti-Lutheran or devoutly Catholic. Among these, Johannes Cochläus, one of Luther's fiercest enemies, wrote twelve; Thomas Murner, the most restless, sharply satirical, and, of the opponents of Luther, probably the most widely known, wrote at least ten. Some of the anonymous booklets published between 1520 and 1525 are probably the work of one of these two men. Doctor Johannes Dietenburger, another opponent of Luther, wrote, in 1523–1524, thirteen tracts published by Grüninger in one year. There are five publications by Hieronymus Gebwiler, a gentle and respected humanist who began his career as an educator in Schlettstadt and taught at the school of the cathedral for fifteen years. He left Strassburg in 1525, at the same time Fries did, and continued, as a schoolteacher in Hagenau in Upper Alsace, to dedicate his writings to Roman Catholic churchmen. The rest of the books Grüninger published are on various subjects and are mostly reprints. The pattern is very clear: aside from reprints and the two Ptolemy editions of 1522 and 1525, the books he printed were either by devout Catholics and non-political, or, if religious, anti-Lutheran. Grüninger was the one staunch Catholic among Strassburg's great printers.

His position was precarious, sometimes amusing. At a time when Cochläus complained that there was hardly anybody who wanted to print pamphlets against Lutheranism, Grüninger, who was one of the few in Germany and the only one in Alsace and Strassburg who did, asserted in Murner's *Great Lutheran Fool* in 1522 that nobody could reprint the book for five years or sell it in the Holy Roman Empire if reprinted afterwards. When the magistrate banned the book, Grüninger wanted to save the rest of the edition and declared, "I have printed it since I must make my bread and butter through printing. I printed it as nobody's foe and nobody's friend." [25] On another tract by Murner, "Whether the King of England or Luther is a Liar," also of 1522, Grüninger printed:

In praise and honor of God the Almighty, in deference to the authority, I, Johannes Grieninger, have printed this little book hoping that nobody will blame me although some people told me I should let somebody else print it. I wish every God-fearing person would remember that I must make a living by printing this or other things.

One has doubts that Grüninger, during these years, was serious in thus asserting his impartiality and his humble pursuit of his trade. His publications and their authors, including Fries, stood in Germany for anti-Lutheranism. In *Karsthans*, one of the most widely read of popular books ridiculing false pretenses among Catholic clergymen, the reader was told that he could get books about popery from Grüninger in Strassburg.[26]

The number of tracts and pamphlets published in Germany during the early twenties is amazing. No fewer than 3,113 polemic writings had been identified by 1870 as having been written in the German language between 1518 and 1523; this number is continuously augmented as new titles come to light. That the public no longer bought many good books is illustrated by Froben's report that Augustine's *De Civitate Dei*, a bestseller during the first two decades of the century sold only one copy at the Frankfurt fair in the fall of 1524.[27] Grüninger's printing also became more careless during the twenties, which was very detrimental to the ambitious project of publishing a Ptolemy edited by Lorenz Fries in 1522 (pp. 41–44). Fries was dissatisfied with it and happy when Grüninger printed another edition of Ptolemy, in 1525, this time for one of the finest publishers in all of Europe, Hans Koberger of Nürnberg, and in collaboration with one of the most famous humanists in Germany, Willibald Pirckheimer of Nürnberg, who was to translate the Ptolemy. True to his publishing policies, Grüninger wanted this Ptolemy to be "pretty and quite small in size for the layman, so that he could carry it in his vest pocket," he also wanted at least five hundred copies in German. He intended, however, to make this Ptolemy accurate, correct, and beautiful, and he wanted to please Pirckheimer.[28]

The agreement to publish this new edition must have been made toward the end of 1523.[29] All through 1524 Grüninger worried about illustrations on the maps and problems of cutting Greek letters or getting Greek type. The delay of manuscript pages in reaching him from Nürnberg lost him much of the summer of 1524, with the result that he did not have the Ptolemy ready for the Easter fair in 1525.

Through the winter, he was also getting the blocks cut for the *Carta Marina*, and hoping that Pirckheimer would write a book to go with it. It was impossible, though, to get the sheets of this large map ready for the Easter fair, let alone a book to explain it. In the first two weeks of March the struggle between the humanistic and conservative position of the publisher and the scholar in Nürnberg on the one side and the practical and businesslike attitude of the printer in Strassburg on the other reached a climax. When Pirckheimer got the final proofs of the first sheets he was so disgusted with the illustrations that he called them carnival scenes. He remarked sarcastically that without the irrelevant illustrations Grüninger's much-talked-about "new" maps would be mainly blank spaces, that the book was for children and the uneducated, and that Albrecht Dürer had looked at the illustrations and laughed in ridicule. Pirckheimer felt that his reputation had been impaired by Grüninger's combining scholarly work with old wives' tales and paintings by playing-card makers. There was just one thing to do, in Pirckheimer's judgment: burn the whole edition.[30]

In response to this, Grüninger wrote two letters on March 10 which read as if he had sat down to write them immediately after receiving the letter from Pirckheimer. In his long answer to the illustrious statesman, scholar, and patron of arts, Grüninger protested repeatedly and vehemently against his decorations' being likened to playing-card pictures (*Kartenmalery*) and flatly refused to burn the edition.[31]

In the still longer letter of the same day to Hans Koberger, the publisher, Grüninger insisted that the public wanted books with decorations, that he had tried to follow instructions from Nürnberg, and that he was going to print a register — an index — for the Ptolemy, no matter what the cost to himself.[32]

Pirckheimer naturally resented the blunt letter from a printer he had never regarded highly, and Koberger must have let Grüninger know Pirckheimer's reaction, because the old printer apologized in a somewhat pitiful letter in which he calls Pirckheimer "Your dignity." [33] Grüninger was in a bad situation. The messengers were slow and it was expensive to keep the workers in his house waiting for corrected pages from Nürnberg. Strassburg was in an uproar, the Saints' days were no longer observed, the shrines and fonts had been broken in the churches by mobs, the villages wanted Lutheran preachers, and there was a rumor that Zwingli had been slain in Zürich. [34]

The Ptolemy of 1525 could have been one of the greatest editions: most of its maps originated with the first Strassburg edition of 1513 and thus are in some way not yet clearly recognizably linked to Waldseemüller; moreover, the translator was one of the great German humanists. But this edition had the same shortcomings as that of 1522 — pieced illustrations, many errors in printing, and poor pagination. The blocks for the fifty-one maps were still valuable and must have been sold by Grüninger or his son after 1529; they were used again in the Lyon edition of 1535, edited by Michael Villanovus (called Servetus), and in his second edition of 1541 which was printed at Vienne in Dauphiné by Gaspar Trechsel. [35] In 1514 and 1519, editions of Ptolemy appeared in Nürnberg and Cracow without maps. Pirckheimer and Koberger were right in their conviction that a better Ptolemy could be printed in 1525 only with the maps from Grüninger's press; by 1529 the Ptolemy of 1525 was sold out and Grüninger was considering the idea of another edition. [36]

As we learn of Grüninger's experiences with the printing of the Ptolemy in 1525 we become aware of a peculiar circumstance regarding the *Uslegung* and the *Carta Marina*: during the months that he was printing the Ptolemy, he also printed the twelve sheets for the *Carta Marina* and tried to find a cosmographer who would write a book to accompany the map. In spite of the bitter feelings between them in connection with the Ptolemy, Grüninger asked Pirckheimer, probably at the beginning of May 1525, to write this companion volume. He even offered to spend a full year on the printing, only one form a day if necessary. We do not know what answer he received from Pirckheimer, if any. No cosmography, only a guidebook called *Uslegung,* was ready on the evening of the Nativity of St. Mary, the eighth of September 1525, and Lorenz Fries was its author.

LORENZ FRIES

HE country of Greece is an extensive region which includes eight realms, Dalmatia, Epinum, Hellas, Thessalia, Macedonia, Achaea, including the two islands, Candia and Ciclades. This country is under Turkish rule but still has several religions. A great number of Jews live there and many Mohammedans. The Greek people are Christians very much of the Lutheran type, only a little more steadfast in their faith and not so envious and rebellious; they do not break their vows as easily as some run-away monks. Greeks have always been an arrogant people and always had contempt for all other countries in the world and ascribe all wisdom to Greece alone. And from there the rot has come into our Germany. Nobody might now be considered a scholar unless he is a *Grecus* and can write with chalk on a wall . . . As if a man's knowledge is in a language and not in his intelligence.[1]

Thus Greece is described, not without prejudice, by Lorenz Fries, clearly not a humanist to be ranked with scholars like Beatus Rhenanus of Schlettstadt or Jacob Wimpheling of Strassburg.

We know no more about Fries's life than about Grüninger's.[2] But we have his portrait, set in a circular frame. It shows a serious face with searching eyes, a long elegant beard below a firm mouth, and a fine, narrow nose, against a monotonous background of horizontal lines; there are no instruments, books, or initials to tell more.[3]

Fries was born about 1490, possibly in Mühlhausen where his family name is recorded, but more likely in Metz where a "Pierre de Frison" is registered. He called himself Laurentius Phryesen of Colmar on the title page of the first two editions of his most famous book, *Spiegel der*

Artzney. The fact that he lived in Colmar when he wrote this book, between 1517 and 1518, but put Argentariae after his name on his next publication when he was in Strassburg, suggests that his identifying himself with one city or another during his life tells us nothing of his place of birth. But he is generally known as Lorenz Fries of Colmar; his name is also spelled Friess, Frisius, Phrisius, Phryes, or Phrijsen, and his famous contemporary, Paracelsus, called him Phrusius. An early attempt to link his name with Friesland and some mistaken associations between Fries and Gemma Phrisius, the famous geographer and associate of Mercator, have added to the confusion.[4] His biographer's idea that Fries may have gone to school in Swabia because of a detailed description of "margt-Grieningen" (Mark-gröningen) must be rejected. This description does not appear in the first edition of the *Uslegung* in 1525 and is probably Grüninger's insertion.[5]

We can safely assume that Fries as a student was a traveling scholar who studied at different universities, one of which may have been in Vienna. He describes life in that city, its good food, and a discussion of astrology overheard at the university.[6] He may also have studied at Piazenca and Padua, and at Montpellier in France, which he regarded very highly and where he may have obtained his doctorate.[7]

He must have come to Colmar around 1516, at about the time he published his first tract about the gallic disease in Latin.[8] He appears to have been proud of this first publication, which we know of only indirectly.[9] When a new "cure" was found in the juices of guayac wood brought by the Spanish from America to Europe in 1508 and known in Germany by 1517, Fries wrote a German tract about this miraculous new treatment for syphilis, recommending it rather than the dreaded mercury cure.[10]

Fries must have observed many cases of syphilis in Colmar, where he helped his good friend the friar Dieboldt Vögelin take care of the sick poor at St. Augustine's monastery.[11] Fries had a strong desire to help people and the considerable courage to break with the medical tradition of professional secrecy. He was much interested in drugs, felt that "a town needed a pharmacy even more than a flour mill, necessary as that was," and understood that internal medicine should be separated from surgery.[12] Grüninger had printed, around the turn of the century,[13] the first German books about surgery and the art of distilling potions. Now, in 1517, Johann Schott published, in Strassburg, another and much better German book on anatomy, illustrated with two large woodcuts drawn by a good artist, Hans Wechtlin, and commemorating Dr. Wendelin Hock's dissection of a body in the presence of doctors and barbers, the first such dissection in Strassburg.[14] The favorable reception of this book caused Fries to hasten the completion of his *Spiegel*, which had no chapters on anatomy because the reader "could go out and buy another book about it," as Fries wrote, seemingly with some regret.

In Strassburg, only forty miles from Colmar, Grüninger was as eager to print books for the lay market as Fries was to help the "common sick" people. The folio volume was ready on September 1, 1518, just in time for the fair at Frankfurt. This home remedy book has a woodcut on the title page which had been designed in 1516 by Strassburg's most famous artist, Hans Baldung Grien, as an illustration of the commandment, "Thou shalt not bear false witness." It shows a sage in academic robes seated in a majestic armchair with two men in front of him, one listening, the other talking with vivid gesticulations. It easily fools even the informed reader,[15] and viewers of 1518 might readily have imagined the seated man to be a dignified medical scholar who could help them to make their own diagnosis from the *Spiegel* which, thank goodness, was in German! The book must have sold very well; a second edition was ready for the fall fair in 1519. By 1546 seven more editions had appeared and the book was used in Alsatian homes for another century at least.[16] It established Fries's reputation in medical history as the author of the first German book on internal medicine.

According to the most noted German historian of medicine, the best edition of the *Spiegel* is the fifth of 1532 because the first four editions were hurriedly printed with many typesetters' errors.[17] Fries was quite perturbed with the book and wrote in 1530: "When I saw it for the first time I thought I had given birth to a sea monster, because so much in it was wrong and torn apart by an unlearned typesetter, and not only that, but he also added many crazy pranks." [18]

Fries was a scholarly physician, proud of his learning, who based every piece of advice on medical authorities, mostly Hippocrates, Galen, and Avicenna; the close connection, in his time, between medicine and astrology shines through in many passages. For instance, he says that well-tempered complexions are found in the middle latitudes; that man is subject to the Moon for the first four years of life and then to Mercury, Venus, Solis, Mars, Jupiter, and finally Saturn; and that health changes with such environmental circumstances as the winds from four and twelve cardinal directions. The pestilence is caused by evil vapors and a conjunction of Saturn and Jupiter. The crisis in illness can be judged by the physician after consulting the constellations. In the end of the book Fries quotes his favorite metaphor, an old Alsatian popular saying: "An old barn without mice and a medical doctor without astrology are the same." [19] On the whole, the book, when compared with writings by contemporaries, shows less coarseness, cruelty, and superstition.

The *Spiegel* was no small achievement for the young doctor who had decided to continue his literary career in Strassburg.[20] His next publication was "a clear guide to words ascribed to herbs, roots, flowers, seeds, minerals, juices and other things in medicine, in Hebrew, Latin, Arabic, Greek and several German tongues," a title which suggested a linguistic ability greater than the author commanded, since it contained only a few misspelled Hebrew words and no Arabic terms; its linguistic pretensions later brought ridicule down upon him.[21] For reasons that are not clear Grüninger did not have it ready until late 1519.[22] Fries was not discouraged, but wrote the tract about natural springs already announced in the *Spiegel*.[23] Among the fourteen spas he lists in southern Germany and Switzerland, Baden-Baden, Ems, and Wildbad are still famous and popular. He also gave advice about diets to be followed at the spas, drugs to be taken, and the mineral or chemical quality of the springs; he strongly objected to eating while one was actually in the water. Grüninger issued this tract on August 9, 1519, decorating it with a woodcut by Erhard Schlitzoc which shows four men and a woman sitting together in a large bathing pool listening as a fool in a cap entertains them by playing a violin. But alas, across the basin, on a board, wine and bread arc laid out before the bathers.[24]

Fries must almost have written this as he traveled. He left Colmar early in 1519 for a visit to Strassburg, which probably included a talk with Grüninger who would have sworn by his faith — and we have seen that Grüninger did not take his faith lightly — that he was very sorry for the foolish work of his typesetters.[25] Fries went for a time to Fribourg, in Switzerland, as a city doctor, but was back in Strassburg by November 29, for he appears as Frisius Argentariae on the title page of the *Synonyma* which Grüninger printed in November 1519.[26]

Fries decided to settle in Strassburg, became a citizen through marriage, and also was a member of the Guild *Zur Steltz*, which was not unusual for doctors because of the traditional connection between art and drawing and medicine.[27] He married Barbara Thun, the daughter of a glazier, Ambrosius Thun, and they had a family about which we have no details.[28] We know nothing about the financial arrangements between Grüninger and Fries, but Fries cannot have earned much from the practice of medicine, for he spent too much time on his writings, which tended increasingly toward astrology, cosmography, and geography.

That the connection between medicine, astrology, and cosmography is old is illustrated by Hippocrates' first chapter on Airs, Waters, and Places, which discusses the healthfulness of various cities in different climates. Fries expressed the need for a knowledge of geography in the practice of medicine thus: "Cosmography teaches the doctor the climates and especially the different countries. If he ignores these he runs the risk of treating a man from northern countries in the same way as one from southern latitudes. What is good for one can be bad for the other." [29] Being a doctor meant, during the Renaissance, being an astrologer. The portrait of the Veronese Hieronymus Fracastorius shows this doctor, the world's first epidemiologist, with a pocket astrolabe. Albrecht Dürer showed how diseases are related to stellar disturbances. The doctor's one assistance in childbirth was reading the horoscope while midwives ministered to the mother. Every doctor had to be able to interpret constellations. Fries knew how to handle the astrolabe, and often dated his writings by referring to the signs rather than the saints. He probably wrote prognostications every year, and certainly after 1523, since those for 1524, 1525, 1526, 1529, 1530, and 1531 are known. [30] Fries's professional conviction that bloodletting, purges, and certain medicines could be prescribed effectively only when the physician understood the constellations got him into religious polemics.

Martin Luther declared, in his sermons on the ten commandments, that astrology was a superstition condemned by God; Fries answered with *Ein kurtze Shirmred der Kunst Astrologie* (a short defense of the art of astrology). [31] In this defense he complained that the arts of arithmetic, geometry, music, and astronomy were in danger of extinction because everybody wanted to study Luther and not the classics, which brought him ridicule from many sides. A polemic pamphlet, *Munarus Leviathan*, appeared, in which Thomas Murner and Fries as a sorcerer conduct a silly dialogue; Pamphilius Gengenbach wrote a satiric play, *Gouchmat*, in which a doctor pretending to be an astrologer is recognized as "that Fries" and ridiculed as a master of black art. [32] The play was probably performed in Basel at carnival time in 1521 and Fries must have become widely known as the doctor and astrologer who was in the same camp as Thomas Murner. Though Fries was not deeply interested in religious problems, he continued the controversy and inserted a sharp reply to Gengenbach in his prognostication for 1524.

Thus Fries and Grüninger were both known as anti-Lutherans, which made them unpopular among most of their fellow citizens in Strassburg during the early twenties and drew them together more closely. In spite of the "sea monsters" which Grüninger's men had made of the identical first two editions of the *Spiegel*, Fries published all that he wrote while he lived in Strassburg, with one minor exception, through Grüninger's press; and Grüninger asked Fries to assist in the preparation of Waldseemüller's maps.

We do not know when in 1520 Grüninger began to talk with Fries about Martin Waldseemüller, whose splendid large maps had sold well, but who no longer came across the mountain divide from St. Dié to Strassburg at carnival time. Grüninger published the second edition of the *Carta Itinerariae Europae* in 1520 and he had on his mind the many designs, already cut, prepared for the *Chronica Mundi*, which Waldseemüller had planned. The *Chronica Mundi* was to be different from Ptolemy's *Geographia*, on which Waldseemüller and Ringmann had worked very hard, but which Oessler and Uebelin had published in 1513 through Johann Schott without mention of Waldseemüller. Now, in 1520, Schott published that *Geographia* again, with only Uebelin left to edit it. How Grüninger could have embellished such a Ptolemy with the material he had! One might even visualize Fries and Grüninger discussing their projects in front of one of the wall maps by Waldseemüller, an office decoration Grüninger would have liked. Both men had great admiration for Waldseemüller's work, and never ignored the deceased geographer's contributions as Oessler and Uebelin had done.

That Fries had ready access to the 1507 Waldseemüller wall map in

1520 becomes apparent from his participation in the publication of Johannes Camers' edition of the ancient *Polyhistor* of Solinus.[33] Though the cost of preparation of the new map was borne by Lucas Alantse, a Viennese bibliophile, Fries's participation is obvious from the initials L.F. in the lower right-hand corner of the accompanying world map: no investigator has doubted it, even though Peter Apian's name appears in the title of the map. The map is clearly very much reduced from Waldseemüller's wall map of 1507.[34] For many years it was noted as the first world map with the name America on it, a tradition irrevocably shattered in 1901 by Joseph Fischer's discovery of Waldseemüller's two large world maps. We are not concerned here with Apian's unjustified claim to the authorship of the map,[35] but for an assessment of Fries's work as a cartographer it is important to note that his first map was a great and rather good reduction of a wall map of 132 by 236 centimeters to one 28 by 40.7.

Adding an item of medical interest, Fries wrote on the map near the island of Spagnola "where guayac is found." And across the new continent, shown as an island, the following legend in Latin appears in block print: "In the year 1497 this land with its adjacent islands was discovered by the Genoese Columbus upon orders of the King of Castille." [36] The same Latin inscription, but without the wrong date, appears on the Tipus Orbis map in Ptolemy's *Geographia* of 1513, suggesting that Fries was familiar with that work. But he did not have sufficient time or astuteness to coordinate the information found on the Tipus Orbis map of 1513, where the date 1492 appears in connection with a legend for Spagnola, and the information on the plaque at the lower left of the Waldseemüller wall map of 1507, where Amerigo Vespucci and his voyage of 1497 are discussed. We shall see later that Fries did not clarify the question of the true discoverer of America in the *Uslegung* either. Although the possibility that Apian was responsible for the inscriptions cannot be entirely ruled out, it appears that Fries began his career as a cartographer by learning how to reduce a map on which the right discoverer but the wrong date appear over the name "America."

An interesting problem which cannot be solved is why Fries collaborated with Apian. Bagrow suggested that Grüninger got the idea of asking Fries to undertake further editions of Waldseemüller's work from Fries's 1520 reduction of the wall map of 1507.[37] One can also suggest the opposite — that Fries got the idea from Grüninger and communicated it to Apian, for Grüninger had a great weakness for new editions in reduced size.

We know only approximately when Grüninger obtained the blocks for the Ptolemy maps from Schott: soon after the publication of Schott's second edition of 1520, because Fries could not have begun the work on Ptolemy before Grüninger was assured of the blocks, which, as we saw, he would not loan out at any price afterwards.[38] Fries must have given the Ptolemy all his time during 1521. He had no Greek manuscript, but employed the translation by Joachim Angelus, drew three new maps, and also used Martin Waldseemüller's *Carta Marina* of 1516, from which he took many inscriptions. Grüninger very likely showed Fries with pride the proofs of the "merry prints" which had been prepared for the *Chronica Mundi* begun by Waldseemüller but would be used on the maps in Ptolemy: kings on thrones, cannibals, elephants, and even a rhinoceros.[39] The initials would all be new and in frames showing the instruments that a cosmographer uses — plumblines, planimetrical astrolabes, the cross-staff, maps of horoscopes, quadrants, sundials, and portable astrolabes.

During the winter of 1521 and 1522, Grüninger's press worked on little else but the Ptolemy; the splendid folio volume just had to be ready for the Easter fair. So Fries hurried "for the sake of friendship." It might even have been Grüninger who suggested placing the Eighth Book in sections between the new maps; he wrote two years later when the *Carta Marina* was in preparation that maps and text "should help one another." Fries had little time to discuss the project with his friend Thomas Vogler, called Aucaparius, who wrote the preface of nearly two pages dated January 10, 1522.[40] Besides explaining at great length what Ptolemy meant to geography and how navigation had helped provide knowledge of the earth, Vogler called Amerigo Vespucci the discoverer of the New World and its islands and eulogized Fries's new maps. Fries said three years later that his Ptolemy was not really "right," but he still saw no need to be ashamed of his work in spite of the calumny, the "nachred," of scholars.[41]

The fifty folded maps and the one of Lorraine printed on the verso of the Tabula Nova Norbegiae and Gottiae have been listed elsewhere.[42] The first of these three, Orbis Typus Universalis Iuxta Hydrographorum Traditionem, has L.F. and 1522 in the banderole across its top. Though this map is obviously reduced from the Orbis Typus of the 1513 edition, because North America is not shown; it has no flag at the island of Isabella, as Apian's map and the 1507 wall map have, and there is one difference for which this map became well known: the name "America" is printed on what looks almost like an island of North America cut off by the right edge of the map. In South America the word "cannibales" reappears from the Ptolemy of 1513; but not the picture from the *Carta Marina* of 1516. A smaller reproduction of this picture, a "spirited woodcut of cannibals feeding on human flesh," as Harisse aptly describes it, appears on the Tabula Terre Novae. It is modeled after Tabula Terre Incognita of 1513, has F D W (Fecit Doctus Waldseemüller), in the banderole across the upper margin and has more inscriptions than the Ptolemy of 1513.

This two-page sheet of the Tabula Terre Novae deserves special mention. Its paper is a little stronger. Its printing is very careful and in minuscule type, different from the humanistic type used throughout the rest of the book. Its Latin is good. Its borders are carefully and symmetrically set with elegant roofing for the upper and a sarcophagus for the lower centerpiece. An initial featuring a sundial starts the story of Christopher Columbus, who can be assumed to be the figure on the woodcut on the verso. In beautiful garb, he has received a gift which looks like a scroll from a pleasantly smiling native who is swimming back to his boat anchored off shore. The map has pictures of the cannibals and of a strange animal, and shows various islands in the western ocean, some with legends for their products. It does not show the name "America." It seems possible that this page, so carefully executed, was also sold separately. In the edition of 1525, which was printed from the same map blocks, this page is not printed in gothic minuscule type. No bibliography of Ptolemy mentions this remarkable difference in printing, but it deserves special attention because the map must be ascribed to Martin Waldseemüller. The four pages are a fine tribute paid Waldseemüller by Grüninger through a remarkable exhibition of his craft, and they are the most beautiful pages in the Ptolemy Fries edited.

The products of the new lands as Waldseemüller had put them on the 1516 *Carta Marina* Fries brought into the 1522 Ptolemy. Four of the old Ptolemy maps — Tabula Europae VIII (Sarmitia), Africae IV (Interior Libya), Asia VII (Scythia), Asia IX (Gendrosia) — have inscriptions which are the same as on the *Carta Marina* and in the same places. One of the characteristic figures sitting in front of a pavilion also appears on the Tabula VII of Asia. In designing, Fries must have had other models besides the four of the "modern" tables of 1513, namely for Gallia, for Germany, for the map of Hungary, Poland, Russia, Prussia, and Wallachia, and for Lorraine. For these Waldseemüller's wall map of Europe has probably been used.[43] The influence of the *Carta Marina* works with full force on the two maps of Africa and the three maps of India.

A third example of Waldseemüller's influence on Fries's Ptolemy is the map of the Holy Land, copied with the inscription "iste terra est fertil," though other inscriptions are necessarily shortened because of the reduction. But in the text Fries wrote: "You know, dear reader, how with emphasis and bragging such great fertility has been ascribed to this land, the same which on the basis of experience of merchants who came from far away is found uncultivated, infertile and lacking in good care, and politically a promised land but not praised in the native language." This sentence, included by Michael Servetus in his Ptolemy edition of 1535, is erroneously said to have been used as a basis for the accusation of heresy against Servetus, the famous doctor who put forth the theory of pulmonary circulation.[44] That Waldseemüller or Fries or both thought badly of the fertility of Palestine's soil is supported by a similar passage on Judea in the *Uslegung*, to be discussed later.

Fries's independent contribution is eight folio pages in which he informs his readers how "sphere," "parallels," and "horizon" are defined, how the earth is measured, what "latitude" and "longitude" stand for, and other things that one should know about cosmography. At the end he gives instructions for measuring the distance on maps and selects an example from close by: the distance from Ulm to Augsburg on the modern map of Germany, another possible link with the *Itineraria* of 1511. There is much in Fries's — i.e., Grüninger's — first Ptolemy that forms a bridge between two ways of viewing the world, and between the earlier and the later, unfinished work of Waldseemüller.

Printing this Ptolemy at his own expense, Grüninger outdid himself. It contains fifteen woodcut illustrations, 10 by 14 or 9 by 13 centimeters. None is repeated, which is in itself unusual for one of his books. The splendid borders, though not always well balanced on the page, were designed by artists outside his firm.[45] Despite the shortcomings that led to negative evaluations by contemporary scholars as well as by historians, the 1522 Ptolemy is without doubt a truly outstanding book.

Grüninger must have written to Koberger in Nürnberg before February 1524 about the idea of publishing a *Chronica Mundi* jointly with

Koberger, but he never mentioned Fries in connection with this plan. Fries did not have a geographer's curiosity about the newly discovered lands; he considered himself instead an astrologer-cosmographer, and his next work was the *Expositio Ususque Astrolabii*, published on September 8, 1522, about the use of the astrolabe for determining the critical days of an illness. After that, he published a small tract in Latin and German about ways in which one could practice the art of memory. In the first chapter, the author asks people to buy this little book, saying that nobody seems to want large volumes any more.[46] This curious book was followed by the aforementioned prognostication for 1524 in which he reported briefly on twelve German towns, ten of which he was to describe in the *Uslegung*. Most important of all, Fries reassured the reader that the "cruel conjunction" of Jupiter and Venus, expected for February 25, 1524, would not be the day of another deluge or of the last judgment, and invoked in support of this his "prophets," Ptolemy, Albumazar, and Aristotle.[47]

The year 1524 cannot have been very satisfactory for Fries if he wanted to continue as a serious writer. In spite of the scholars' cool reception, his 1522 edition of Ptolemy had probably sold fairly well, since Grüninger turned to Koberger in Nürnberg for assistance with a new edition less than two years later. Grüninger was in poor financial condition and glad to get a large printing order from Nürnberg; he might also have felt that his beautiful decorations warranted another edition, translated this time by a great scholar. Though he wrote in February that "Dr. Fries is well disposed toward me," it is possible that he was a little too confident. Three months later, on June 1, 1524, he wrote, concerning the problem of correcting the Ptolemy, that he would have to call in Doctor Fries and he did not like to do that. This was the first year since they had become acquainted that Fries had not prepared a manuscript for Grüninger to print. His only publication of 1524, *Der Juden Practica*, a prognostication which is reported to have been a sharp condemnation of the Jewish people, was published by Armand Farckall at Hagenau.[48]

During the same year, men in Strassburg like Fries, Thomas Vogler, Hieronymus Gebwiler, and Grüninger found themselves increasingly on the defensive against the Reformation. Fries gave up writing entirely except for his prognostications, and devoted his time perhaps to medicine and to the reduction of the *Carta Marina* about which Grüninger wrote Pirckheimer.[49] Grüninger expected to sell each set of the *Carta Marina* for five gulden, and tried hard to persuade Pirckheimer to write a great book to accompany the map. Only after all his pleas had fallen on deaf ears did he ready his press to print the short *Uslegung* as a guide to be sold with it; he must have finished both around March 12, 1525.[50]

Early in 1525, the storm of religious and social revolt was sweeping through Germany and the Peasants' War became a direct threat to Strassburg. The city's authorities were openly sympathetic to Lutheranism and even Roman Catholic clergymen had to go to the Pfaltz to have their names entered as citizens according to the order of January 26. It would be an error to think that the entry of the names of good Catholics like Thomas Vogler and Hieronymus Gebwiler implies enthusiasm to become citizens of pro-Lutheran Strassburg. Gebwiler is recorded as leaving the city in 1525. And Fries abdicated his citizenship on Thursday, May 11, 1525.[51] His reasons are not documented anywhere, but we can surmise that he found the religious situation there intolerable.

News of the worst slaughter of the Peasants' War, at Zabern, came the following Tuesday. Thus Fries probably departed at the height of the Peasants' War, leaving a 1526 prognostication for Grüninger to print and going to Metz, where he stayed less than three years. In February 1528 he was in Colmar, where he temporarily received Paracelsus, then a fugitive from Basel, into his home. By July he was in Diedenhofen in Lorraine, probably again on his way to Metz.[52] He styled himself a doctor and mathematician from Germany "temporarily residing at Metz" on the title page of his prognostication of October 1528 for 1529. This year also saw his bitter controversy with Paracelsus.[53]

In 1529 the "English sweat," an unidentified epidemic, crossed the Channel into Europe and the Bishop of Strassburg requested instructions for precautionary measures from Fries and the city physician of Metz, Jean Brunnon. The little tract, *Sudoris Anglici Exitialis . . .*, apparently written solely by Fries, appeared in September 1529 in Strassburg. In March 1529, Grüninger had published the third and probably the worst edition of the *Spiegel*, and in 1530 he issued Fries's prognostication for 1531. From Otto Brunfels' introduction to the 1532 edition of the *Spiegel* we know that Fries had died earlier, probably in 1531.

Fries's five years of wandering among Strassburg, Metz, and Colmar, issuing incidental publications in German, Latin, and French through different printers, are in striking contrast to the stability of his literary production while he was a citizen of Strassburg working with Grüninger. The old printer worked to his last year and also died about 1531. His firm was continued at first by his sons and subsequently operated reputedly in the same quarters in the Schlauchgasse until 1894, under the internationally famous name of Heitz. Wherever his establishment, Master Johannes Grüninger had, for at least seven years, stored in it copies of the *Carta Marina* and notes for it left behind by Martin Waldseemüller, without which neither the *Carta Marina* of 1525 nor the *Uslegung* would have been published. It is obvious that Fries's poor copy of Waldseemüller's original has little cartographic value and is not a subject for the exercise of careful comparison of sources. But for the history of the geographic education of the public the map has significance. Using the reproduction in the pocket of this book, we shall compare it with the 1516 model and evaluate its content.

THE MAP AND THE BOOK

HAVE tried with my modest ability . . . to put the map in pleasant size according to rules and accurate geometric measure. Not that I want to diminish, depreciate, or disparage the other which was made earlier by the world-famous Martin Waldseemüller, bless his soul, as envious people may easily accuse me of, but because the said *Carta Marina* would not be any good or useful for anybody because of its superfluous length and width. I request that you [Grüninger] be my witness for this apology. I do not want to devaluate or diminish any scholar, nor his reputation or art, be he alive or dead.[1]

The *Carta Marina* of 1525 is of "pleasant size," as Fries put it, and preserved in one copy at the state library of Bavaria at Munich. The twelve sheets are bound in a folio volume without a note or signature on the binding to tell where it came from. No history of its acquisition is available, nor could anything be learned about the circumstances which prompted the firm of Ludwig Rosenthal of Munich to produce a facsimile in 1926, without an explanatory text. An examination of these large sheets quickly reveals that an evaluation of the map is possible only if one works with it as it was meant to be used, as a wall map. Mounting copies of the sheets is an experience worth the effort, because one shares it with the buyers of the map in the third decade of the sixteenth century.[2]

This was the first indexed wall map of the world printed in German for German laymen (*Leut*, people, as the publisher would call them); it was not meant for scholars.

a	b	c	ծ
aa	bb	cc	ծծ
aaa	bbb	ccc	ծծծ

Every edition of the *Uslegung* had the same instructions and a diagram which explained what was to be done with the *Carta Marina*. Fries presented "instructions how to glue the map on linen and how to make the pages fit" as follows:

If you want to mount the map yourself and glue it, take a linen cloth or a piece of a clean old linen sheet and put a broad board on a table or chest and stretch the sheet firmly with nails hammered in all around. After that cut the pages along the left side so that they fit each other. The middle sheets, aa etc. must be cut off also lengthwise. You should try their fit before you start to glue. After that put some glue, but not too strong, into a little pan. Warm it up, but not too hot. Then take a brush, not too small and with soft bristles. Put the pan on the board on which you have stretched the linen and then take the first sheet, labeled a. Turn it around and brush the back with glue and put it on the upper left hand, the way one writes a and then b. Have somebody around to hand you the pages so that you can put them on fast and so that they fit immediately. Then put a clean paper over it and rub it with a piece of cloth so that it is smooth . . . Particularly cut the bbb sheet to the left exactly to the coat of arms.[3]

This diagram, appearing under the instructions at the very end of the book, was of some help, but probably not much when it came to fitting the sheets. For example, the West Africa sheet is 374 millimeters high and should fit East Africa, which is 371 millimeters high, which in turn should fit sheet dd, which measures 375 millimeters. The artistic frames and heavy black borders vary in width but could be considered last in mounting the map. The equator, however, a pronounced double line, must be continuous across four sheets, and the continental outlines must also join. Differences of a few millimeters are important here, and readers who have had experience with instructions for do-it-yourself projects in the twentieth century will sympathize with the assistant in Strassburg in 1525 who had "to hand the pages" to a man who had just spent five gulden for the set.

The sheets of the Waldseemüller *Carta Marina* of 1516, upon which Fries based his *Carta Marina*, did not fit any better. They were of a similar height, and Fries had reduced the width of the map proper about ten per cent. But because of differences in the widths of the borders included in the map as a whole, Fries's map measured 1,876 by 1,013 millimeters as compared with Waldseemüller's 2,480 by 1,335. In considering Fries's reduction, we can omit the borders and the three sheets of the column on the left, for these were not involved in the reduction. A further problem is the uneven width of some of the individual sheets. The ten per cent reduction in width was largely attained by narrowing open spaces, particularly ocean areas, which could be done without altering the height of the map. Fries was truly concerned with decreasing the width only, as he said in his preface.[4]

His map presents a narrower-looking southern Africa, a narrower South Atlantic ocean, and narrower Indian peninsulas. The outlines of coasts and the courses of rivers are all included, but they are cut more clumsily than their counterparts on the Waldseemüller map, and present a less elegant appearance. The reduction also affected the legends, for less room was available, and in addition there was the fact that German, printed in gothic minuscule, was used in place of Latin in humanistic print, thereby consuming more space for the same legend. Fries therefore shortened most of Waldseemüller's legends as he translated them, leaving the engraved Latin inscriptions intact. Fries's *Carta Marina* also looks somewhat unfinished, because all three shields in the lower left section have no inscriptions. Obviously there was no sponsor for the map; Grüninger printed it at his own expense, so the shields which might have contained a sponsor's name were empty. The fact that the map was not proofread meant that the space of the largest shield used on the Waldseemüller model for suggested corrections was empty on Fries's map. However, these blank spaces invited handwritten dedications, making the map an appropriate gift.

		WIDTH OF COLUMN (mm)	
	column b	*column c*	*column d*
1516 map			
upper tier	526	540	593(543)
middle tier	500	539	595(540)
lower tier	519	532	592(543)
1525 map			
upper tier	470	469	526(469)
middle tier	479	480	524(468)
lower tier	475	485	527(468)

		HEIGHT OF TIER (mm)		
	column a	*column b*	*column c*	*column d*
1516 map				
upper tier	413(364)	418(364)	415(359)	418(365)
middle tier	364	373	372	370
1525 map				
upper tier	406(364)	404(324)	407(320)	402(331)
middle tier	355 *	363–374 *	371	375

NOTE: Size excluding borders is given in parentheses.

The comparison in the tabulation above of the individual sheets of the *Carta Marina* of 1525 with those of 1516 shows the amount of reduction Fries made, and suggests the problems of fitting the sheets together for each map. Since the sheets in column a and those comprising the lowest tier are of little importance to these problems, they are omitted. The difficulties in fitting the sheets arise chiefly with respect to the width of the sheets depicting West Africa, which are in column b. For the three sheets of the 1525 map in this column we find

* These sheets present no great problem of fitting or reduction; the mapped areas of the northeast coast of South America are adjustable because of the illustrations that ran on these sheets.

a variation of 9 millimeters, for the 1516 sheets 26 millimeters. The task of joining the sheets is considerable with such great variation.

This discrepancy calls for a closer inspection of the twelve Waldseemüller sheets of 1516. When the set was discovered, it was bound, with one sheet lying loose in the volume. This loose sheet was a second map of West Africa, a clean copy, but full of printing errors. Apparently it was from this model that Fries worked. The West Africa sheet bound in the volume is a slightly reduced hand tracing by Waldseemüller on which all the mistakes of the loose sheet have been corrected. This tracing is 516 by 365 millimeters, only 10 millimeters different from the adjoining sheet (compared with 26 millimeters for the loose sheet). Though this tracing does not eliminate all irregularities, it brought the West Africa sheet closer to the width of the adjacent sheets. It seems that Waldseemüller intended not only to correct the misspelled names but also to make a better-fitting sheet when he made the design for the new block.

An important feature of the Waldseemüller's sheets Fischer and Wieser discovered (see page 40) is the rectangular grid which is drawn in red ink under the black block print on all twelve bound sheets, that is, eleven printed maps and the tracing. Fischer and Wieser conclude correctly that these maps "afford us a glance into the workshop of Waldseemüller." [5] The grid is drawn through many legends and extends to the frame, but it is not completed in the ocean areas. It could serve for purposes of reduction, but it was doubtlessly designed for the development of an index for the map. The tracing has the grid, whereas the printed copy for West Africa has not. Waldseemüller drew the grid first to have the print laid over afterwards, probably because the strong paper and heavy blockprint could cause the ink to run and the pen to slip. We do not know whether he came to Strassburg to do this or sent prepared sheets from St. Dié to Grüninger. It is more likely that he came to Strassburg because the work needed supervision.

The grid is laid out in degrees which begin at Porto Sancto, one of the Madeiras, and extend 173 degrees to the east. There is an interesting omission of nearly twenty degrees between sheets c and d. The handwritten numbers 90 and 115 on the sheets reveal the mistake; actually the degrees from 94 to 113 are left out. Another omission is that of the climates in the left-hand column; in the lowest tier on the decorative sheet there is no vertical column for latitudinal degrees. This means that no indexing of place names would be possible for Brazil, South Africa, and Java. The incompleteness of the vertical column for degrees of latitude could be corrected by inserting such a column. This is easily done on wood blocks. But it would have spoiled the frame of both small shields and the dedication to Bishop Hugo, whose name and title are printed around the shield outside the frame. Finally, to the west, or left, the longitudinal degrees go from 280 to 360. An attentive person would easily realize that this map does not show the whole world. To the uninformed — and the map was meant for the general reading public — it meant a clumsier and more complicated numbering system for the index. Thus the set of the Waldseemüller sheets as it has been preserved certainly was not ready for issuance as a wall map for which a book with index numbers, called a register in the *Uslegung*, could be published simultaneously. It is also noteworthy that the person who had the twelve sheets bound into an atlas, together with twelve sheets of the Waldseemüller wall map of 1507, used the Waldseemüller tracing rather than the printed copy of the Africa sheet as part of the whole map.

That person was Johannes Schöner of Nürnberg.[6] Since he used sheet remnants of his globes of 1515 and 1517 for the inside of the backing, the binding of the large sheets must have taken place after 1517, probably after Waldseemüller's death. There is no indication of any association between Waldseemüller and Schöner, but it is plausible to assume that Schöner obtained the set from Willibald Pirckheimer, for he was one of the few people whom Pirckheimer trusted toward the end of his life. Also, he was charged by Pirckheimer's heirs with making a catalog of Pirckheimer's very valuable and extensive library, notes, and collections. Through Grüninger's correspondence with Koberger and Pirckheimer we know that some *Carta Marina* material of 1516 had been sent to Nürnberg. Who but Grüninger could have shipped this set to Nürnberg? Ringmann, Duke René of Lorraine, and Waldseemüller were all dead; and the new Duke of Lorraine had no interest in geography. Grüninger had other notes about the *Carta Marina* from Waldseemüller, for we saw that Fries used *Carta Marina* material for the Ptolemy of 1522 and shall see later how much Fries must have used notes by Waldseemüller for the *Uslegung*. Pirckheimer was supposed to compose the great *Chronica Mundi* in Latin, and Grüninger, who wrote that he was even willing to sell something in order to be able to finance a proper index for a Ptolemy, would want a practical, usable index in the book that was to be sold with the wall map. The grid, an absolute necessity for such an index, was the part of the *Carta Marina* of 1516 which Waldseemüller had worked on but not finished. A reference by Pirckheimer in the 1525 edition of Ptolemy to the plan to work on plane maps with parallel meridians suggests that he was somewhat interested in the kind of map the *Carta Marina* presented.[7] The preserved set of Waldseemüller's wall map of 1507 was no longer of any use to Grüninger because it had grid lines on two sheets. He quite possibly could have sent the 1507 set along also as another sample of work which must be undertaken for purposes of indexing or reducing.

Grüninger was always ready to publish German and Latin editions of the same work as well as abbreviated new editions of items that sold well. The *Carta Marina* of 1516 was as large as the 1507 map, about eight feet long and four and a half feet high. Such a map had sold well in 1507, but folio volumes were beginning to sell less well every year;

to be popular, wall maps had to be smaller. Fischer and Wieser assert that the *Carta Marina* of 1516 was much less widely distributed than the wall map of 1507. The latter had a very great influence on other mapmakers, but the authors mention only one sixteenth-century reference to the *Carta Marina* of 1516, in Ortelius' *Theatrum Orbis Terrarum* of 1570.[8] This reference is not specific; it could even mean only that Ortelius knew indirectly through Fries's *Uslegung* that Waldseemüller had edited such a map. Why did not Sebastian Münster copy something from the *Carta Marina* of 1516 in his famous *Kollegienbuch*, when he copied ten separate maps from the *Itineraria* of 1511 by Waldseemüller and two maps each from Waldseemüller's 1507 wall map and the Waldseemüller maps in the Ptolemy of 1513? Even if the maps in Münster's *Kollegienbuch*, which August Wolkenhauer established through careful investigation to have been composed mainly between 1515 and 1518, are difficult to date and are partly earlier than the *Carta Marina*, Waldseemüller's map of 1516 should have interested Münster enough for some copying of Southeast Asia, whose third Indian peninsula, shown on the wall map of 1507, had disappeared by 1516.[9]

This is another illustration of the strange fact that Waldseemüller's new world map was little noticed by contemporaries. Fries's much more poorly executed *Carta Marina* was published at least three times in five years and Münster used the *Carta Marina* of 1525 and the *Uslegung* for his own *Cosmographia*. Fischer and Wieser are of the opinion that Gerhard Mercator used the *Carta Marina* of 1516 for several of his works.[10] It is not possible to investigate here if Mercator could have derived from Fries's copy the same details that prompted Fischer and Wieser to assume this influence of Waldseemüller's *Carta Marina* on Mercator. Schöner's reference to "cartis marinarijs" in his *Opusculum Geographicum* is not very convincing either.[11]

In summary, it is not unreasonable to raise the question of whether the *Carta Marina* of 1516 ever reached the market; in view of the aforesaid it is unlikely.

We are not certain whether Fries used or saw Waldseemüller's working set of the *Carta Marina*. At first glance it would seem that Fries must have seen it, because he misinterpreted two lines that look like one double line on the reproduction of Waldseemüller's map, and put in its stead one heavy straight line running east and west through the wind rose directly above Oceanus occidentalis on sheet a and sheet b. But we must remember that this double black line on the reproduction results from the original red-inked line of the grid plus a black rhumb line from the wind rose. We could assume then, that Fries simply drew only the east–west rhumb line through the wind rose in the same location. This, however, leaves unexplained the second heavy line across sheets a and b, which also corresponds to a double line on Waldseemüller's map resulting from parallel grid and rhumb line. Here Fries has no rhumb line emanating from a wind rose, but only this meaningless heavy line, the result of some misinterpretation.[12]

In addition, Fries inserted the missing degree column on the sheet with the shield and he made a new grid. He was not bound by Canerio's map which had served Waldseemuller as a model when he counted 173 degrees eastward from Porto Sancto and from 270 to 360 degrees to the west.[13] Fries counted 360 degrees from 0 at the left straight through to the right, under a double line, with white and black interspaces. He put the numbers 10, 20, and so on to 360 in the middle of each group of ten such interspaces, which are 50–51.5 millimeters wide. Thus there was no longer any longitudinal indication on the *Carta Marina*. The numbers from 1 to 360 could give uninformed viewers the idea that 360 degrees — that is, the whole world — were presented on this *Carta Marina*, which is not based on a projection, but is a quadratic plane map without a net of graduation.[14]

Fries omitted the few indications of longitudinal degrees which Waldseemüller had put in along the equator at 15, 35, and 360. This omission was rather a service to the uninformed user, because he would not have known how to relate these numbers to the numbers 0 to 360 at the upper border. Fries also used the word *grad* (degrees) for his instructions:

So that you will understand it all the more easily I will tell you how to find quickly all things named on the map. Do this: look up in the following register, which you will find in alphabetical order, your country, your region, your island, your city, or whatever you want to know. On the map you find two numbers for degrees. You look for the first at the left hand. Then where the number is, put a string and hold it across the length of the map. Do the same with the other number. Look for it above among the degrees and where the number is let a string hang down with a lead weight attached. Where the two strings cross each other you will find the place or city that you want to know.[15]

These degrees are nothing but quadratic coordinates on Fries's map and have, because of the changed horizontal numbering, lost their connection with longitudinal degrees. Modern geography recognizes the completely arbitrary selection of the location of a prime meridian; for centuries having it situated in one's country was a matter of prestige. But the Strassburger of 1525 certainly was not ready for a discussion of the best location of the prime meridian. His great problem was to learn to live in a global world for which 360 longitudinal degrees on the map implied a size that in reality was about one third larger than that shown on the *Carta Marina* by Fries, who veiled this fact with his numbering system. Waldseemüller's map, even if 100 degrees were missing from it, would have been more instructive. For the mapmaker to show this missing part of the world was totally out of the question, for several reasons. Fries did not have the zeal or the courage to incorporate new knowledge on the *Carta Marina* of 1525 — the circumnavigation of the globe by Magellan, for example. Waldseemüller could

The Map and the Book

not know of it in 1515–1516, the last years of his work on his *Carta
Marina*.[16] Grüninger could not be expected to add between 1½ and 2
feet to the "superfluous length and width" of the map. What legends or
decorations was he to put on this part which would largely be ocean,
when his *formenschneider* (formcutters) were singularly inept at cutting ships, sea monsters, and mermaids? The little notice on the en-
closed legend in Brazil, under the equator — about "the interior of this
land, that we have not yet explored"— was the viewer's only clue that
there was much to discover about the world in the area where the
decorative shields covered ignorance.

Reduction, even by a small amount, necessitates omissions where
the map is crowded.[17] The place names are sometimes easier to read on
Fries's map than on Waldseemüller's because there are fewer of them.
Also, in crowded areas where a slip of the engraver's knife could ruin
an adjacent word, abbreviations of place names were the natural solu-
tion. It is essential, therefore, that we not apply modern standards of
accuracy to maps of this period, for if we do we create false problems.[18]
Warnings against such wasteful exercise of learning have been issued
occasionally.[19] They were heeded in this study only after much strain
of the eyes in comparing the names on Fries's and Waldseemüller's
maps. The *Carta Marina* of 1525 "abounds in strange misunderstand-
ings and mistakes," and the comparison of names proves somewhat
rewarding only in one location — the coastline of Africa.[20] On both
Waldsccmüller's and Fries's maps, the names are engraved along the
coastline, jutting into the restricted land area instead of into the open
ocean, and following each other closely. This identical arrangement
of names on both maps, in the tradition of marine charts, should make
it possible to detect a system of omissions on Fries's map — if indeed
such a system exists.

This arrangement inside the coastline makes the names even more
crowded when the maps are reduced. From Strictus sibilie (Gibraltar)

on the Waldseemüller map, or Strictu sibillie on the Fries map, to Cape Periodias, the last name on sheet bb, Waldseemüller has 179 place names and Fries has 98. This is the part of the coastline that is most affected by a reduction in width. A group of ten consecutive names is left out by Fries, from "alberne" to "sette can." Capo Debozador at the northeastern corner of West Africa is among the names omitted, for no good reason, because there is enough open space here. We do not know whether Fries or the engraver forgot this group of names or part of it. In addition to this negligence, four consecutive names are omitted at one point and three names at two others along the West African coast. Thirteen pairs of consecutive names are left out and thirty-two single names, at regular intervals. This suggests considerable regularity in omissions along this part of the West African coast — thus the omissions were not entirely accidental.

Along the South American coast, negligence on Fries's part appears responsible for the omission of five names. Altogether, he correctly copied twenty-nine names for rivers, landings, and islands on the first South America sheet, extending from Lixleo to Cannibales. He omitted .P. Dearena, began with Santa Maria, and continued to Porto Seguro. Though there is space for them, he then omitted five names, perhaps because he found that he was already putting names too far south, below the Tropic of Capricorn. Below Serra de .S. Thome he left out five more of the ten names Waldseemüller had had along the southernmost end of South America's coastline.[21]

Fries had to omit a number of names in Europe, particularly along the Adriatic coast. Here the names, printed upside down, are hardly legible on Waldseemüller's map, and the device of printing names along both sides of the coastline — on the land as well as in the ocean — would still not have made it possible to get every name engraved into the smaller space, particularly since Grüninger's letter engraver of 1525 was not so skillful as the one of 1516. There were no Moses on Mount

Sinai, no Hungarian flag, and at one place in Africa he condensed two legends into one. Generally, Fries's legends fill their frames, whereas Waldseemüller's Latin ones were often too short to fill them. The frames for the legends took up more room on the 1525 map because Grüninger wanted them to be attractive, and therefore decorated the simple outlines of 1516 ornately with curves and borders and actually hung them by hooks from the equator. One addition of 1525 was a banderole in the blank space next to the crescent in South America on which *Dz nüv erfunden land* (the new found land) was printed. The reader was spared the inconvenience of reading names printed upside down as they were on Waldseemüller's map along Arabia's and Africa's Red Sea coast, and the legends for Mecca and Medina were considerably shortened for lack of space. The frame in which Calicut had been described at length by Waldseemüller was much smaller and contained a shortened legend which did not note the many products of this region but did have a brief addition: "Known until recently only to Venetians, now better known through Portuguese navigators who found a new route." Praise of the King of Portugal was also added near the Cape of Good Hope, but the legend for Spagnola about Christopher Columbus was considerably and ineptly shortened. Two inscriptions were added in South America; one told about cannibals, the other, mentioned earlier, said that the coast had been navigated but the interior had not yet been explored. Fries's or a typesetter's negligence printed 1510 for 1501 as the year of the discovery of Terra laboratoris, an island to be discussed later (pp. 73, 81), by Corte Real. "A larger book from which more could be learned" was mentioned in the largest legend, at the lower right. An outline for the island of Scotora, called "Cacotoria sive Scutora," off the Arabian coast, is not shown; but "Scotora" is printed on the mainland—another case of negligence. All outlines are simplified and more clumsily cut than on the Waldseemüller map. The rhumb lines between sheets bbb and ccc do not fit, because sheet ccc has six whereas sheet bbb has eight lines extending to the northwest and west. Thus the map of 1525 is of uneven quality, but as a wall decoration it is an artistically more balanced picture of the world as it was then known than were the composite of the sheets in Waldseemüller's set.

The twelve sheets of Fries's map as they have come to light are uneven in another respect. This set is a combination from at least two, possibly all three editions. The long Latin inscription above the upper frame across all four sheets reads: "Carta Marina navigatoria Portugalien naviga. atq: tocius cogniti orbis terrae marisq: forma. naturam sitq et terminos noviter recognitos et ab antiquor tradito et differentes hec generaliter monstrat 1525." The German title in the *Uslegung*, which Fries offered for those who were more likely to read the German legends than the Latin, reads, in translation: "An ocean map of Portuguese navigations and of the whole known world; of the earth's and oceans' outlines, of nature, opportunity, and regions. Once more newly improved and different from the old representation here generally presented — 1525." [22]

There can be no doubt that the map was also issued in 1527.[23] The 1527 edition of the *Uslegung*, which contained all the references to the map, would not have been practical without a second edition of the map. That the map was also issued in 1530 is certain. Sheet dd has Grüninger's warning of 1530 that the map was protected by imperial privilege and could not be reprinted for the next five years under penalty of a fine of ten gold marks. The large Latin inscription on the lower edge of sheet ddd says that the map was based on truth and edited by "Lorentio Frisio" in 1530. The appearance of the date 1530 carved a little below the inscription suggests that this date was a later insertion.[24] Both sheets show signs of wear and some rhumb lines are broken. Grüninger certainly would have taken the trouble also to correct the date in the title for the 1530 edition, since he corrected the date in the signature. We are thus certain that at least two editions, those of 1530 and 1525, are combined in this map.

Watermarks provide no reliable means of dating editions. Because other printers in Alsace and Basel had difficulty getting paper during these turbulent years,[25] Grüninger probably had to get paper from several mills, particularly when he needed a large supply in early 1525 for printing this map and the Ptolemy. Nine of twelve sheets have the same watermark — an oxhead with a pointed cross on a staff above — but the sheet with 1525 on it has a fleur de lis. The South America sheet, bbb, has an anchor in a circle. The Africa sheet is of heavier paper than all the others and has no watermark.[26] The frames are not uniform either; they are fitted together and were probably designed by different artists. In spite of the *Uslegung*'s statement that Europe "is distinguished by a different color on the map," no trace of coloring is found on the set at Munich.[27]

To summarize: It is certain that the one extant set is a combination from at least two different editions. Engraved names and sentences were of poorer craftsmanship than the printed legends.[28] Though Fries's Latin is poorer than Waldseemüller's, he is not to blame for all the mistakes on his map. We have come to know him well enough as an astrologer not to hold him responsible for calling the line of the southern equinox the Tropic of Cancer, rather than Capricorn; making Terra de Cuba a part of Africa also was probably the doing of the typesetters.[29] We saw what they did to his *Spiegel der Artzney* in 1518 and 1519. Fries was probably not given a chance to proofread a copy and had possibly left Strassburg when the maps, most likely five hundred sets, were printed for the fall fair in 1525.[30] He added only minor details to the map and abbreviated many inscriptions by simply omitting sentences rather than condensing the contents. But his translations were acceptable; all of them were of such a length as to fit well into their frames, whereas Waldseemüller's legends were often too short to fill them. The print with large gothic initials is, indeed, "merrier" to look at than the undifferentiated humanistic print on Waldseemüller's *Carta Marina*. In fact, Fries's world map is altogether artistically superior.

The best figure is the Portuguese King Emanuel, who appears as master of the seas and rides around the Cape of Good Hope on a sea lion which looks strong but tame. The movement of this figure, the swift design of waves, the fluttering flag and robe, the grasp of the hands on sword and scepter, and most of all the animal itself remind us again of the school of Grien.[31] The figure is superior to the king on the map of 1516, where Emanuel was not yet bearded, but a muscular young man wearing a breast plate. The second drawing which attracts attention is an animal with a pouch pictured next to cannibals in South America. The cannibals are even more "spirited" than they were in 1522 and 1516, although in drawing technique they are strikingly similar and probably by the same hand; the fabulous animal with the pouch looks more content here than in 1516: it is nursing a young one. "The big animal which lives in Norway and has square feet"— a sort of cross between a European bison (Aurochs) and elephant — looks about the same on both maps. But in 1525 a whole family of "anthrophages" on the great island of Java are about to feast on a human being whereas in 1516 one poorly drawn specimen is engaged in this gory work. The big Chan near Cambalu (Cimberlay or Peking) sits in front of a more beautifully decorated pavilion than had his counterpart in 1516, and his hands hold a sword and scepter more gracefully cut. Two riders, one on a reindeer to the north of the Chan, the other on a horse to the west of him, galloping toward the land of the Tartars, give the same impression of rapid motion as did their predecessors in 1516. The brother of the Prince of Cassan, who also rules from the entrance to his pavilion, looked happier in that year; but in 1525 he is crowded into a smaller tent. The two rhinoceroses are about the same, though the later one is perhaps a little more ready to charge. The elephant in the "new part of Africa," south of the Mountains of the Moon, is no better than the one of 1516, and neither can compare with the beautiful specimen on the wall map of 1507. There is only one additional animal on the 1525 map: in South Africa one basilisk is squeezed between names along the western coast and a straight mountain range, whereas Waldseemüller's map had two. In addition to the animals and the major designs, Grüninger also had the following small scenes or figures on the map of 1525: Another anthrophagus in interior Asia, three scenes of people with dog's heads, one man with only one eye, one with two uneven legs, and one with his head on his chest (it would be a long time before Europe would stop feeding its imaginings about far-away lands and peoples on the writings of Solinus and the other fabulists who followed him). A widow is being burned in King Banzales' realm but the viewer is assured, perhaps by a typesetter's idea of humor, that "women in this country when they lose their men, go into the fire willingly and full of hope." The "little people," the pigmies, are shown fighting cranes in the land where there is much pepper — in the northern Indian desert which the King of Portugal found in 1495. In Mongolia, three men in tall felt hats are engaged in a discussion. Far to the north, in the land of the Sameodares, a man is trying to club a swiftly running hare; to the right of this scene is a kneeling woman who according to the inscription is a "parositar" and does not eat cooked meat.

Between 1516 and 1525 Grüninger deployed a veritable army of engraved kings throughout the two wall maps and in his editions of Ptolemy. He could have used smaller monarchs from the large-scale map as big kings on the small-scale map — if the term scale may be applied — but all figures were cut anew and smaller for the map of 1525. All kings have what a Strassburger thought kings should have: crown, scepter, and throne. In Asia, they sit in front of pavilions and wear jeweled felt hats. Prester John in Ethiopia has a tiara with two crosses; kings in Senegal and Gambia have modest crowns, simpler thrones, and no robes. Only the kings of Pego (Pegu) and Deccan are different: they have no thrones and are standing up. The *formenschneider* of whom Grüninger wrote in 1524 must have been able to carve kings of any size freehand and needed no designs for this mass production. Paul Kristeller's contention that in Grüninger's studio designers and woodcutters were not distinct from each other is supported by the striking uniformity of subject, style, and technique.

Almost all the pictures of the *Carta Marina* of 1516 — which shows King Emanuel, six animals, twenty-one scenes, and thirty-eight assorted other kings — appear also on the map in 1525; it lacks only one basilisk, two small kings, and one very small group scene.

Even if some of these figures look crude — and many are not crude at all — people must have liked them, for many other maps of the time have these royal figures. A noteworthy precedent are the strikingly similar-looking kings on Martin Behaim's globe, which was illustrated by George Glockendon of Nürnberg.[32]

The borders are artistically the most important part of the *Carta Marina* of 1525. The different expressions of the faces in the border can best be appreciated when the map is turned all around. The hat worn above the realistically drawn face at the east-southeast, the bitter miens of the winds in the north and the merry round faces of those in the south, the treatment of clouds and the elegant bordures for the names of thirty-two winds are the work of a master. There is an initial below the shield "west" next to the column for latitudinal degrees, nine degrees south of the equator. It is an F encircled by a cord, but no identification is possible. The sections of the border have obviously been fitted together and need not be by the same artist, but all are the work of masters.[33]

Fries put flags where he found them on the 1516 map and omitted only the two to the east of Africa because too much space was taken up by the frame with the legend for Calicut. It was probably he, rather than an engraver, who was responsible for the incomplete system of rhumb lines, the faulty placement of compass roses, and the departure from the authoritative and elaborate system of the wind rose. The roses were much better done on Waldseemüller's map, where the central rose of the whole map, in interior Africa, had thirty-two spokes and looked like a ship's wheel as it should, since it was used by mariners on the "ocean seas." Not that the system worked, because of the declination of the compass needle; but Fries's wheel with its thirty-six spokes is a wagon wheel, as are his others, particularly the one that hangs on his mysterious heavy line in the Oceanus occidentalis, which he somewhat unnecessarily translated as the sea toward the setting sun. If Waldseemüller misunderstood the role of the crescent in South America on Canerio's map and used it for a wind rose system, Fries knew even less of the lore of the sea.[34] His explanation was probably not very enlightening to the equally land-minded burghers of Alsace.

Everywhere on this map lines are drawn through the ocean criss-crossing each other, which seems strange to some people. To explain this briefly: you should know that these lines do not mean anything else than the needle by which mariners steer their ship from one port to the next they want to go to. Accordingly they know how to go in and out of the wind. And if through some misfortune they are thrown off their intended course, they know by means of the aforementioned lines in the midst of the ocean, where they see nothing but sky and water, how to get back to the right route. All this must be done with the help of astronomical instruments on the basis of these lines.[35]

As for the treatment of water and waves, one cannot be certain whether this was left to the skill of the cutter or drawn by Fries. Waldseemüller drew no shading or waves on the ocean area on his tracing of the West Africa sheet. The ocean is treated the same on sheets a and bbb, but differently on all the other sheets. On Fries's map, the treatment of clouds in the ocean areas is good for the North Atlantic, but so poor between Africa and South America that islands and clouds are hard to distinguish. On all other seas, the scorper technique of shading along the shore is used.

At times Fries took extraordinary care to copy small details — for instance, the three small crosses between Cape Pruno and Cape Rotundum in the big bight of the southwestern coast of Africa. One wonders if he knew that the crosses meant shallow waters where boats could easily run aground, because he put the cross symbols too far away from the shore along the east African coast. The coastline, particularly around the island of Zanzibar, was very poorly outlined; but Fries missed no religious symbols: crescents for Mohammedanism in Africa; the big cross for the kingdom of Nubia, where, according to his legend, the Jacobites lived; and a smaller cross in "Upper India" next to a wind rose.

The technique of showing mountain ranges is probably a little better on Fries's map than on Waldseemüller's. Fries frequently uses them to divide political realms, a peculiar and not yet fully understood attempt to delineate regions by natural boundaries. The compartmentalization of land areas through divides is easily recognized for five regions along the upper border, "Morduarii, Hungaria, Parosi, Samoderum, desertum magnum." Sometimes a region in central Asia, characterized by a scene with a written explanation, is set off from the next by a mountain range. But just as a crescent does not mean that the designer believed that a quarter moon actually would be found in a certain place, winding mountain crests do not necessarily mean that the cartographer believed in the existence of these lines of mountains. Men like Waldseemüller and Fries who had traveled across the Vosges and the Alps knew very well what mountains were like; so did the traveling *formenschneider* and printers. These mountains are symbols to indicate divides in the same way that crossed axes are used to indicate a mine on our best modern geological quadrangles. For example, the mapmakers knew very little about the East Indian peninsula, ruled by King Bagmani, but somewhere in the middle of it there had to be the height of land from which rivers would flow in opposite directions to the seas. The kingdom of Calicut is set off from India Magna and the kingdom of Narsinga from that of Deccan by such mountain ranges, and similar treatment can be recognized in Africa. Some ranges have only one apparent purpose: to show where rivers start, among which the one along the Guinea coast of Africa is the most obvious.[36] While pictorial symbols were used, the practice of explaining them in a systematic key did not yet exist, though explanations were sometimes given rather incidentally. Waldseemüller, for instance, in his *Cosmographia Introductio* of 1507, which was meant to be a schoolbook, supplied some explanations on the verso of his map of a globe: "I have marked with crosses shallow places in the sea where shipwreck may be feared." And Fries, in the eighth chapter of the *Uslegung*, explained that circles were signs for towns. This did not, of course, preclude the use of more imaginative symbols for cities.

The use of such imaginative symbols illustrates man's habit of imagining the unknown in familiar terms.[37] On the *Carta Marina*, towns have walls, turrets, and gates, and are small versions of Alsatian cities, be they in the African kingdoms of Melli and Ethiopia, or in Calicut and Murfuli in southern Asia. The larger design of a walled city with turrets, high gables, and battlements for Cambalu (Peking) could as appropriately be used as an illustration of a German town in a different book. Of towns everywhere only Mecca does not have a western European look. On the sheet for western Europe, where their actual appearance was known, towns could not be depicted. Here the familiar symbol of the circle appears, used by Waldseemüller on the wall map of 1507 and called "ringlein" by Fries. This serviceable symbol to pinpoint the actual location of a town with a precision that can never be achieved by the printed place names alone is still used on modern small-scale maps.

The dotted lines for roads are as disappointing on Waldseemüller's map as on Fries's. Although Fries explains that these are "well-known roads outside of which no one may travel" one looks in vain for continuous dotted lines to show the great international trade routes from which it would be dangerous to stray. Such dotted lines had been used on *itineraria* (the road maps of the Roman Empire),[38] and were a useful device by means of which one could compute distance by counting the dots between two stops; this method probably was never quite forgotten and was later used for the charts of pilgrims and, by 1500, for road maps.[39] Dotted lines are still used for caravan routes on many modern atlas maps of Asia and Africa. Waldseemüller showed the *via maris* in Palestine from the Mediterranean to Jordan and Galilee in this way on the map of the Holy Land in the Ptolemy of 1513. He did not use dotted lines for the wall map of 1507, but must have drawn them on the *Itineraria* of Europe in 1511, for which he used Erhart Etzlaub's map of 1501. Etzlaub made a road map of the German Empire with Nürnberg as a center from which roads led radially in all directions. These roads were represented by dotted lines; the legend at the bottom of the map explained that the number of dots between two cities corresponded to the number of miles between them.

Only a few such dotted lines appeared on the *Carta Marina*: in extreme eastern Asia; around the Gulf of Finland, where Lappia (called apia) was surrounded by such a line; along some mountains, such as the range surrounding Calicut; in the foothills of Narsinga in India; and along rivers. But through Asia only a few disconnected lines showed caravan routes, and none led across the western Sahara Desert, where old routes had long been known to exist.

Rivers were shown by double lines, as was usual on maps of this period, and the vegetation shown was at best decorative. On Waldseemüller's maps the varying appearance of the trees on the island which Corte Real discovered in the northern Atlantic probably resulted from two different engravers working on the two sheets (a and b) the island straddles; it does not mean that trees were believed to be different on the windward and leeward side of the large island. Fries copied this difference. He also copied trees in western Africa in the region of the Hesperides, and misspelled Hesperis, who, according to legend, were nymphs guarding the tree bearing golden apples. The drawings do not show fruit trees, and the legend tells the viewer only that in this great wilderness dwell tigers, leopards of different colors, elephants, parrots, seraphim, ostriches, and marvellously big ants. Trees that look like pines represent the savanna habitat of Africa's fabulous animals, and the same kind of tree symbol serves in northern Asia to represent forests from which "across this whole northern latitude precious furs would find their way to the western parts."

This inscription, like most of the Latin inscriptions on Fries's map, was engraved. There were a few exceptions — the small Latin legend east of Arabia concerning the island of Ormuz, where pearls were reported to be found, and that for the island of Scutora (Socotra), reported as having been conquered by the Saracens in 1507, both of which were printed. All German legends were in gothic minuscule type, whether they were decoratively framed or inset without any bordering lines. The engraved Latin inscriptions are far less readable than the German insets. The latter were probably more eagerly studied by the people whom Grüninger had in mind when he wanted a German translation by Fries of the Latin map by Waldseemüller.

What kind of world would this map portray for a citizen of Strassburg, Worms, or Augsburg in southern Germany? Joseph Fischer, the scholar who discovered the *Carta Marina* of 1516 and investigated its sources, interpreted not only Waldseemüller's original but also Fries's copy as "the oldest printed map of missions" of the world. He thought that Martin Waldseemüller was an indefatigable Christian who intended to publish a German edition also, since a German map would have been more suitable for promoting a world missionary spirit.[40]

The main argument in favor of the motive of showing the work of Christian missions which Fischer attributed to the map of 1516 no longer pertains to the map of 1525; Fries did not use missionary reports such as those of Nicolas Ascelin, the Dominican missionary, and the two Franciscans, Odoric of Pordenone and Giovanni de Plano Carpini, which are among the sources Waldseemüller listed on the large shield of his *Carta Marina*. Fries simply copied what Waldseemüller had drawn and made no noticeable effort to preserve information about missionary work when he condensed or abbreviated legends. For example, in the small sea in northern Asia, based upon Carpini's report, Fries forgot one of the four islands. The framed inset for the land of India says that there are Christians there, but nothing of idolatry and Mohammedans. Whereas Waldseemüller described Prester John as the King of Abyssinian Christians, who practice baptism and circumcision, Fries calls him merely a King of Christians. The long passage in the large framed legend for Calicut, which dealt with religion, is reduced by Fries to a sentence about idolaters. These examples should suffice to show that Fries did not exhibit the missionary spirit that Fischer discerned in Waldseemüller's map.

Rather than pass summary judgment about the meaning of the *Carta Marina* for Alsatian or German viewers in the late twenties of the fifteenth century, let us imagine that, using the *Carta Marina* in this book, we accompany a Strassburger on an extended journey he could have taken with the help of his wall map. Literal translations would be lengthy and probably bore us; but the vocabulary used below should be largely derived from that on the map, familiar to a Strassburger who has looked first at the illustrations and is now beginning the serious work of informing himself about the world, which, according to the title of the map, was becoming known to Europeans through Portuguese navigation. He might begin with the framed table at the lower right corner which promises to tell where spices come from.[41]

Here Fries told the Strassburger where Calicut's spices and goods came from and what weights and measures were used there; pepper came from Korunckel, fifty miles from Calicut, cinnamon came from Ceylon, another two hundred miles away, and cloves came from Melutza, five hundred miles further on — seven hundred and fifty miles from Calicut.[42] Ginger grew near Calicut, but some was brought from Cannanor twelve miles away. Nutmegs came from Melucha and bisem (civet, musk) from another country five hundred miles away called "Lego." The great pearls came from Armuzo (Ormuz), also five hundred miles from Calicut. After finding Calicut, Ceylon, Cannanor, and Pego but not Lego on the map, the serious student could decipher the Latin legend in the ocean about the fishing for pearls at the southernmost tip of India. He could not find Armuzo, but one of the four islands south of the fishing grounds for pearls was named "bisam."[43] As long as Fries announced that a little book "to be published with God's will as a guide to the map" would explain it all further, the reader might skip the second column of the legend about measures and agree that he had "now a list of the value of goods and small spices which belong in the pharmacies." They were weighed by faracola, a Portuguese unit of about eighteen pounds. Drugs were not mentioned on Waldseemüller's map, but Fries's interest in pharmaceuticals could perhaps be appreciated by the Strassburger who used the *Spiegel* in his home.[44]

The island of Sanda was described as having wild pepper and nutmeg trees and the island of Monoch as a producer of wild cloves. Both islands were between Java and the southernmost tip of the East Indian peninsula. It may have been reassuring to read that "good and sensible people are found in Borneo,"[45] but less so to discover that on Java people sold their parents to be butchered when they could no longer work. Java appeared to have no redeeming qualities in Fries's eyes.

Three legends about the proper location of Taprobana, called Samotra, placed below the equinox as Ptolemy had put it and not where Solinus had, probably held the viewer's attention to a lesser degree. Fries himself did not seem to have clearly understood Waldseemüller's explanation of this problem, but he emphasized that everything there was big and in great supply, as nowhere else in the world, that all sorts of spices could be got from Samotra, and that pepper grew particularly long on this island. The reader could also learn that carbuncles and iacictes grew on Seylan (Ceylon).[46]

Of the mainland of the East India peninsula it could be learned that much brazilwood and sandalwood and many fish were available in the land of the King of Pego. In Murfuli only the eagles who brought up diamonds out of an abyss were mentioned; the Strassburger would read about this in detail in the *Uslegung*. Farther to the north, great hens and roosters without feathers, said to have wool like sheep although the hens laid eggs, were not likely to stir a Strassburg merchant's interest as much as India or the island of Jona, where beautifully dyed silks came from. This island was in an isolated spot far to the south of India, and the legend next to it extolled the merits of Portuguese navigators who had proved Ptolemy wrong when he declared that the Indian Ocean was surrounded by land.

The reports of India were mostly about people. There were idolaters in Narsinga, whose king the reader could find more easily by the river than he could make out the letters of Narsinga scattered irregularly over the interior of India. But idolatry did not prevent Narsinga's population from tolerating many Christians in their midst or from liking the Portuguese. Legends in Latin and German explained that St. Thomas was buried along the eastern coast and that the people in Colon (Quilon), south of Calicut, were also idolaters. Two of the monarchs in this part of the world rode elephants into battle. About Calicut with its fabulously rich trade to which only the Venetians had had access for so long, more could be read in the book, said the legend, and a Portuguese flag told who now controlled that trade.

In present-day Burma, the King of Nella resided and paid tribute to the great Chan of Cathay. The Chan's impressive pavilion must have aroused the reader's desire to find out more about him. Along the eastern shore of the Chan's land the soil was fertile; there lived tame elephants and large fish which threw themselves on the shore and were thus easily caught. His realm was divided into seven regions and had over two thousand cities. In one of the regions, pigmies only five handspans tall made beautiful small things of "samat," which sounded peaceful enough; but it was puzzling that they lived directly next to another people who would eat their own parents.[47] In the great Chan's realm, which people in Strassburg had probably heard of before, the use of separate scripts for old and new laws was reported. Christians were respected there and the people believed in eternal life, but they did not practice baptism. It was a land rich in grain, gold, and silk. Justice was administered from a great palace with four golden columns, where the great Chan was protected by many soldiers, lions, and leopards. Looking at the long east–west expanse of the Eurasian continent, the Strassburger might wonder how many days one would have to travel through the land of the Tartars before seeing some of the wonders that Marco Polo had told about.[48]

The great Chan ruled over all the Asian land, including Mongolia. A sharply drawn straight line was meant to make it clear where control by Indian potentates began and control by the Chan ended. This amazing way of mapping an aspect of political geography was explained by a Latin inscription. But the Indian potentates' control remained ambiguous in the west, since the line was not continued onto the next sheet into Tartaria torenquese.[49] Mongolia, which one would have to cross to get to the wonders at the Chan's court, was depicted as having fertile soil when there was water for irrigation, and land largely good for grazing, but it had very few settlements. Crocodiles far to the south along the Ganges River in northern India and the many fantastic creatures which one could also read about in Mandeville made the borderlands of Mongolia very unattractive. The Tartars living far to the north were known to have neither towns nor villages but lived in tents, moving all the time in search of pasture for their animals. Nothing was known of what lay beyond them to the north in Asia, and the map ended with their land, which extended to seventy degrees north latitude.

The north even closer to Europe was little known. Pilaveland, approximately where southern Finland now is, was a region of precious furs. The dotted line around it told one not to stray from the roads designated for travel by the ruler. Fries's negligence and a typesetter's whim combined to make apia out of Lappia and to present this bit of information: "In Russia there are people like apes." Our Strassburger could not know that Waldseemüller's comment about the Russians in Lappia had been more cautiously phrased: "The inhabitants here are people who have limbs and faces which approach those of apes." The land of Russia, the name of which was printed three times on the map, was ruled by the Prince of Russians and Muscovites from Novgorod, identified on the map by his coat of arms. His crown looked like a miter and he held a scepter and a staff with a Greek cross. Also, the turrets of Moscow were faintly onion-shaped, the typical symbol of Russian architecture for centuries to come.[50]

Toward the Black Sea and Turkey one could see the King of Great Bulgaria and then to the northeast the Caspian Sea, called Mare abacuc or Mare de Sala, the greatest lake in the world, which, in spite of its name, was reported to have fresh water. In nearby Armenia, the Christians were said to be Jacobites.

In the adjacent countries of sultans, caliphs, and King Sophus, the character of the information changed, and the legends, becoming shorter, dealt with Islam and Christianity. King Noy in northernmost Persia, whose pavilion displayed his name like the sign on a store, ruled over Christians and Saracens. Just north of Baghdad, which had its *ringlein* directly by the Persian Gulf, King Sophus was mentioned as the man who rebuilt Persia. In Chaldea, the men bedecked themselves with ornaments, but not the women,[51] though it is doubtful that any Strassburger could decipher this because it was poorly engraved and he was not likely to have the help of Waldseemüller's map. The inscriptions for Persia, "from which one of the holy kings had come to Bethlehem," and for Corosan (Khurasan), where "heavenly bread fell to earth" were reversed from Waldseemüller's map. Directly north of the Arabian mountain range, running straight east and west, the inscription read: "Here is the Indian Ocean, there mummies are found, that is human flesh [preserved] through medical art."[52] The poor printing and the strange German into which Fries had rendered Waldseemüller's respectable Latin might have caused the Strassburger to pause a little before he continued to study the map and crossed the divide between the desert of Arabia and Arabia Felix (the letters "foelix" scattered over Arabia in the usual puzzling fashion), in the direction of the Red Sea, where the towns of Mecca and Medina were indicated by unusual-looking round buildings. The reader was told in Latin and German that Mohammed and his daughter were buried in Medina, that Mecca was a hundred miles away from Medina, and that a great deal of trade went on in its big market.[53]

In East Africa there was much to be read about Prester John of the city of Hamaharic in Abyssinia. To the west of Prester John was the kingdom of Nubia, inhabited by Jacobites, watered by the Nile, and remarkable for its white pelicans. There also dwelt big snakes which made the earth odorous where they crawled. Otherwise the map made no revelations about East and South Africa, but it contained many place names, most of them along the coast. The reader was warned to keep away from the large island of Madagascar, nearly four thousand miles in circumference, and a land of elephants, leopards, and lions where "it is not good to walk . . . without protection." The map was more informative about West Africa. Gold was abundant in the interior, as the Latin legend said, and like the Nile, the long river which flowed almost straight from east to west through the province of Turchoror brought great fertility to the land.[54] Enormous trade in salt was carried on in the kingdom of Melli which was attractively represented by its king, a rhinoceros, and an Alsatian-looking civitas Melli.

All this had become known through navigation along the northwest African shore and through trade with the kingdoms of Gambia and Senegal. Senegal divided the black moors of the infertile land to the north from the brown moors of the fertile land to the south, said the framed legend in the *Sinus hespericus* below the Canary Islands. Next to this legend was another which said that the compass needle had "to be turned around once and then again" by pilots who wanted to sail toward the island group of "chamana secusam."[55] The Strassburger was now south of the equator and perhaps inclined to by-pass the interior along the Guinea coast, even though ebony trees grew there, for this land of Melli was peopled by monopeds and cirripeds.[56] The map said specifically, but in Latin, that between the coast and civitas Melli the one-eyed barnacle-footed black men were tall and horrible. It was clear that Africa did not have many resources and was important mainly for providing stations for taking on fresh water on the way to India, at Capo de bona speranza (Cape of Good Hope) particularly.[57]

There remained the new land called Prasilia in the south. It was also called the land of parrots. According to its framed legend, its interior had not been explored, though ships had sailed along its shore. The cannibals received much attention in three German legends — more than the explorers received in another framed inscription about the

ruler of Spain who had come this far and the Portuguese who came after
him. Our Strassburger would look in vain for the name America in the
region of Terra parias where pearls and gold abounded but men had to
eat snakes and roots. In Spagnola, discovered by Christopher Columbus in 1492, people also ate snakes; gold, mastic, aloes, cinnamon, and
ginger were plentiful here too. Right next to it the engraved inscription
said that the Antilles were islands inhabited by cannibals, and many
crosses placed in the waters between a large unnamed island and the
smaller islands of Babueca, Sanra, and Somento told the user that here
the sea was very dangerous for ships.[58]

It was not much use puzzling over Cuba as "partis affrice" when it
obviously was in Asia. The large island to the north, which a captain
named Casper Corterati (Gaspar Corte Real), with a commission from
the King of Portugal had — according to Fries — discovered in 1510,
did not promise many treasures — only herring and cod.[59] A glance at
the Azores, called "Ilas axagoras" on the map, and another to the north
where it said that much more would have to be found out about Nor-
begia where the *Aurochs* (the animal with the square feet) lived, and
our Strassburger could begin to study the location of places in Europe.[60]

Of all the foreign countries he could learn about from the map, Terra
corterati was the one he would have been wise to study if he could have
seen into the future. This land, said to extend over six hundred miles
and probably joined to the other continent, was inhabited by people
who lived in houses made of tall trees, dressed in skins, and knew no
iron but only instruments made of sharpened stones. The map said that
their faces were "painted like the Indians'," an apt comparison since
further exploration was to reveal that the island was indeed part of the
red men's realm, though in the minds of early fifteenth century Strassburgers it was still linked to India. This was the only reference on the
Carta Marina that applied in any way to that part of the New World
which was to become most important for Germans later on.

No Strassburger took such a long imaginary journey in one sitting, nor in the order in which it has been presented here. Deciphering the legends would take many hours. It also took space to hang a map of 225 by 114 centimeters, and space was often limited in rooms whose walls were paneled and held many cupboards and shelves. His windows, with their roundels, were small, and the hours of daylight short during the winter. But this was the image of the world he could have seen.

Though it said on the map that much remained to be discovered about the north, the Indian Ocean north of Madagascar, and Brazil, much of the world seemed known — only, as we now know, it was not one world at all, but three fabulous parts of the world with a fourth one recently added and each approached differently. From western Europe a transcontinental route took the traveler to eastern Asia via Russia and Mongolia to Peking. Another world was India and the Spice Islands, to be reached by circumnavigating Africa, and the third was Africa itself, with watering stations along the coast and a little known interior. Finally, there were the newly discovered islands along the coast of a mainland to the west, of which only some shores were known. This was to become known as America. This wall map reflected the beginning of a long tradition of world geography as seen by western Europeans and studied in German schools.[61]

Whoever bought the map in Strassburg, Ulm, Augsburg, Basel, or other towns in southwest Germany probably used the *Uslegung* with it, and there read about his own city as well as faraway lands. The map with its many German legends under a Latin title would not be bought by French-speaking people across the Vosges, or in Italy, Portugal or Spain, and the *Uslegung* reflected this regional market as we shall now see.

THE BOOK AND THE MAP

ERE I have explained the title of this praise-worthy work from which everybody can learn, quickly and easily, what the map is about. Now we shall give a clear understanding of every renowned place . . .[1]

The subtitle of the *Uslegung* stated the author's intention of helping every reader find "where he was in the world and where the different countries, oceans, and cities were located." In the dedicatory letter to Grüninger, Fries acknowledged his debt to Waldseemüller and promised an interpretation of the *Carta Marina* that would make the map useful and entertaining. The text was divided in two, the first part consisting of a general introduction in nine chapters, most of which were as pedantic and elementary as his instructions for mounting the map, and a register or index. The second part described selected countries and places in separate paragraphs. Fries described what the reader could see on the map, including its border, in a way that makes it mandatory to read the book and look at the map at the same time. The text is also revealing of the author's point of view and his qualifications to publish not only a popular German version of Waldseemüller's *Carta Marina* but also a guidebook to complement the informative map and make it more practical.

Fries began by pointing out that the beautifully decorated borders show the winds as mariners know them and then repeated the names of thirty-two winds, adding that they are shown by faces "so that everybody may be better entertained." Waldseemüller had drawn a fine pilot's wheel for a wind rose in the center of Africa and had written the names of thirty-eight winds on the scrolls and plaques that were somewhat irregularly placed in the border; there were thirty-four heads in the border, some blowing visibly, but most without lines emanating from their mouths to indicate their activity. Fries drew only a cartwheel with thirty-six spokes to represent Waldseemüller's wind rose, but dutifully copied all of Waldseemüller's thirty-eight winds.[2] But the artist of 1525 drew thirty-two faces, most of which are blowing impressively onto the map, as shown by the straight lines. Only five heads lack these lines, four of them around the upper right corner of the map, probably because the lines would have run into legends. Only one set of lines is clearly missing: "poneno," the west wind, with his magnificent somber countenance in the center of the right-hand border could, but does not, issue wind lines into the map area. Fries explained in the *Uslegung*:

In order to account for mariners and seafaring people having so many winds, not four or eight or twelve as one usually has and the way Pliny says, I tell you that it is done because of the width of the sea . . . It is easy to see that as many winds may be imagined as there are lines. On as wide an area as the ocean one might notice differences more than in narrows, in valleys, and on hills. That is why the mariners have grouped the winds into so many numbers and use them and call them by the names listed above. But the old masters who observed nature have postulated four winds which were then subdivided according to the twelve celestial signs and called by the place from which they blew.[3]

This fits the picture of Fries as we have come to know him. He, in Alsace, could not see much need for a compass rose of thirty-eight winds, and would rather have worked with the twelve signs of the zodiac or the twelve winds as he listed them in his *Spiegel* and follow or copy the teachings of such scholars as Pliny or Aristotle.[4] He revealed, not surprisingly, a landsman's point of view. Though the search for data about his life leaves gaps, we have no reason whatsoever to believe that he ever saw the ocean, talked with seafaring men in a port, or, as a doctor, paid any attention to the effects of ocean air upon people's health. During the age of the great discoveries by Portuguese and Spanish navigators, he preferred to study Ptolemy and prepare astrological prognostications.

Grüninger's world was entirely restricted to a circuit which included Swabia, Frankfurt, and other German towns north of the Alps, often on navigable rivers but not on the sea. Waldseemüller, born in Freiburg, never went even to Italy, and lived in a western valley of the Vosges; he was no man of the seacoast either. This leaves the artists who made the designs, and of them we know little. Aside from the waves which King Emanuel's seafaring animals are stirring up on both maps and in the Ptolemy, only a few pictures in the *Uslegung* show water of any kind. We can only conclude that the venture of presenting the world with its oceans to German readers by means of a wall map, description, and illustrations was undertaken by men with no direct experience at all of the sea.

Fries continued his introduction by explaining his system of coordinates, which he extended to 70 degrees north, "to the highest possible habitat of men." [5] He also "explained" the column for climates, which was probably less clear to him than it had been to Waldseemüller. The latter spaced the vertical coordinate correctly in that his left-hand vertical column was uniformly divided, except that it was missing from the lowest sheet, as we mentioned before. Fries misrepresented Eratosthenes' system of seven climatic zones, spacing them at intervals of 5 degrees, which do not even start at the equator and thus do not proceed by fives but as 2, 7, 12, and 17 degrees north of the equator. South of the equator the column of seven climates begins at 15 degrees south latitude and ends at 51 degrees, which is even less logical.

According to Fries, the ocean "surrounds the whole earth, is called Oceanus because of its swiftness," and is subdivided into seas named after habitable places. All the twenty-eight seas enumerated are ancient, including the Hellespont and the Bosporus; his authority is the writings of Ptolemy and Strabo. In spite of his optimistic final comment that "they can clearly be seen on the map," we find the names only of Sinus Persicus and Sinus Gangicus on the map — for good reason: the map is on far too small a scale to show all the various names of the smaller seas in the Mediterranean, particularly where shorelines are scraped and further obscured by names carved into the water area.

The chapter on the three parts of the world — Europe, Africa, and Asia — is in the classical tradition and therefore seems quite out of place in a book that aims to interpret a map of oceans and Portuguese navigation. No attempt was made to integrate America as a fourth part of this image of the world.

Next, Fries explains the classical basis for climatic zones, that is, the imposition of celestial circles onto the globe, in a very perfunctory way probably traceable to his limited acquaintance with Strabo's *Geographia*.[6] He then enumerates six of the seven climatic zones by names "which they got from the cities which lie along their lines" — diameros from Meroe, diasyene from Syene, and so on to diaboristenes, the sixth climate, "named after a river known as Neper" (Dnieper). Either Fries or the typesetter forgot the seventh. To these seven, "experience of the newer world" had added an eighth, called diatyles "after a town which lies toward midnight and the frozen sea." Fries did not specify the town, which is Thule. On the southern half of the globe the climates have their counterparts with "anti-" prefixed to the northern names. For once, Fries spared the reader another list by writing "and so on" after antidialevandros. He then elaborated on how the climatic zones are used when, for example, a merchant travels from Alexandria to Frankfurt. "Look up the F in the register and then find number 47 in the left-hand column and thus also climate 7." This did not tell the merchant much about the climate at Frankfurt and only happened to work because the number 47 is directly next to "Cli 7" in its arbitrarily set division of 5 degrees. If the merchant had traveled to a place between 16 and 22 or 51 and 60 degrees north, he could not have read off with certainty the number of the climate applicable to these places. Fries probably thought the reader of his guidebook incapable of understanding the evolution of the concepts behind the climatic zones from the time of Eratosthenes to the time of Pierre d'Ailly — if he understood them himself. It does seem that a doctor eager to give practical advice in his *Spiegel* and in the treatise on natural springs might have wanted in the *Uslegung* to enlighten the traveler from Alexandria a little more about the different climate in Frankfurt-on-Main so that he could equip himself accordingly. This lack of useful advice dims a reader's expectations about the practical usefulness of the book and its register, "alphabetically arranged and not by locations."

The next paragraph is also disappointing. "In many places land areas that are not shaded mean islands, some with names, others without, because they have no inhabitants; and small crosses around some of them mean that the inhabitants are Christians or subject to Christian kings." Fries does not seem to have noticed that there were many crosses on his map between unnamed islands. For instance, in the Caribbean area was the aforementioned ship's cemetery and the crosses there might have implied to the unwary reader that there were Christians on uninhabited islands.[7] The coats of arms on flags and the "ringlein" for cities are mentioned also, and it is explained that the countries are spelled out in letters of different size. These letters may not always be found next to each other, but "spread throughout the region of the land," an apt description of this technique, still used in modern mapmaking, but with greater skill than Fries applied in, for instance, the case of Narsinga, discussed in the previous chapter.[8] Mountains and rivers are said to be named, but this is only partly true.

The last chapter in the general introductory section reflects Grüninger's project of a great book with *itineraria* to accompany the *Carta*

Marina, an idea which he had expressed to Hans Koberger even before February 1524, when he wrote him about it again.[9] Fries explained to his readers how such an *itineraria* was to be used for determining the distance between two places, Basel and Strassburg, for example, warning them, however, that "when there are bends in the road and mountains, then add" to the distance. The reader was referred to a scale of miles and told that with his compass he could determine that the distance from Basel to Strassburg was fourteen miles, and indeed, that was the straight-line distance on the map.[10] The distance from Strassburg to Basel, from Ulm to Augsburg and from Alexandria to Frankfurt were the only practical examples of measuring distances that Fries used in his geographical writings. He was not a world traveler, but a geographer who learned from books; he would readily think of Alexandria, Ptolemy's city, and Frankfurt, the prominent book market of Germany. He provided two scales of German miles on the map, and also an Italian scale, but the French scale, which the *Uslegung* says is shown on the map, is not to be found. A reader might have been disappointed also by the absence of Spanish and Portuguese scales, considering that the *Carta Marina* was designed to show the world according to Portuguese discoveries.

These failings might have surprised only a few Strassburgers, for most of them would expect Fries to have limitations because he was an ardent Catholic and associated with men like Thomas Murner. Contemporary readers might also have attributed the shortcomings of the map to the decline in the quality of Grüninger's publications in the twenties. It is likely that anyone sufficiently concerned with world geography to purchase the *Carta Marina* and the *Uslegung* would have known his own surroundings well enough not to have needed Fries's pedantic instructions for finding Strassburg and Basel. He would also have known the location of such nearby towns as Speyer and Worms on the Rhine, though he would probably have been puzzled by the east—west course of the Rhine north of Strassburg.[11] The register would probably have been more welcome to a Strassburger for helping him find cities in eastern Germany, such as Breslau, called Presla, which was indicated in the register as lying at the junction of coordinates 55 and 166 on the map and which appeared at that location, on the Oder. The news of the danger which Christendom faced from the Turks would have aroused interest in the places they had recently conquered. With the register, the reader could find, for instance, the island of Rhodes at the point where the coordinates 37 and 188 crossed. The text told him that this former bastion against the Moslems had a history extending back before Christ and that it had until recently been defended by "the Hospitalers of St. John [who] had received much money from all of Christendom to help them guard the island against the Turks." The sad news relayed by Fries that the Turks had conquered the island may have reminded the reader of 1525 of the talk at the Pfaltz about new ramparts which the city would need if the Turks advanced as far west as Strassburg.[12] The reader who wanted to know how far away was Turkey, the source of Europe's greatest danger, found that the intersection of the numbers 44 and 194 in the register brought him to the very center of the name Turkey.

Thus it is demonstrable that Fries's numbers in the register really worked on the map. It is unlikely that contemporaries followed in their entirety Fries's instructions for finding places on the map. It seems much less practical to use two strings than two long rulers, which are easier to handle in checking a hundred and seventeen place names from the register on the map and vice versa to ascertain the accuracy of Fries's map index.

To produce a map with a grid and a register it was necessary for Fries, Grüninger, the typesetters, and the woodcutters to work closely together, and by and large they were successful. Errors occurred, to be sure, such as wrong location numbers for the city of Taurisium and for the Canary Islands.[13] And there are many variations in spelling between the register and the map; while some place names appeared in German on the register and in Latin on the map, for instance, Brazil is spelt Prisilia on the map, Presilia in the register, and Prasilia in the text.[14] Switzerland and Swabia are not identified on the map, because of mountains and the crowding of place names in these two places. These faults are not very serious and, indeed, did not prevent the map from being both educational and entertaining for the student of geography of the period — and entertaining for the geographer of the twentieth century.

It is not surprising that the *Carta Marina* and the *Uslegung* enjoyed great popularity between 1525 and 1530. In a region where many lay persons received an adequate education in reading their native tongue and, in many city and church schools, some training in Latin, it was natural that the opening up of new areas to European merchants and missionaries should have stimulated a keen interest in the outer world. The result of this interest, and the proof of it, were three German editions of the *Uslegung* and one abbreviated Latin version, with an accompanying four editions of the *Carta Marina*, within five years, all published by Grüninger.[15] It is apparent, therefore, that the *Uslegung* and the *Carta Marina* achieved their purpose of educational entertainment. Intended to appeal to a broad public, they did not attempt to be scientific any more than modern pictorial maps would attempt to include findings of the International Geophysical Year 1957 and 1958. Indexed guides for wall maps are not available in our time, but they might be a useful addition to the equipment of a modern geography classroom. Also, some of the widely advertised map games currently sold in the United States contain errors which seem less excusable than Fries's misspellings.

In addition to the hundred and seventeen places in the register that were also described in the chapters, the register of 1525 contains eighty-one additional place names with at least two location numbers, and five places negligently identified by only one location number, none of which is discussed in the text. Fourteen of the eighty-one were rivers which had two pairs of numbers so that the reader could find "where the water starts and where it ends." Only four mountain chains are listed in the register. Of the eighty-one place names with two numbers, fifty-three were in Europe, fifteen of classical or biblical association, and thirteen recent discoveries, including India. Also listed in the register are thirty names which neither have location numbers nor are on the map, probably because they are all cities, chiefly in Swabia and Alsace and therefore too close together to be engraved.[16] None of these cities is to be found on Waldseemüller's *Carta Marina* and it seems likely that Fries's source for them was the Waldseemüller map of Europe published in 1511.

The text of the *Uslegung* presented usually rather short descriptions of fifty-one cities, twenty-three in Germany, nine in Italy, three in France, one each in Holland, Poland, Portugal, Bohemia, Hungary, and eleven outside of Europe.[17] One chapter was devoted to each of twenty-four European countries or regions, including Russia; twenty-four more were based on classical or medieval knowledge, describing Antioch, Arabia, Egypt, Persia, Ethiopia, Prester John's Land, and Nubia; and only twenty-one chapters dealt with countries that had been revealed in the age of discovery.[18]

A comparison of the registers for the three editions of the *Uslegung* reveals some interesting differences. The registers of 1525 and 1527 do not differ materially from each other, except for some changes in spelling and a general improvement in the appearance of the latter. One noteworthy change was made in 1527 by adding location numbers for Colmar and for "margt Grieningen" (Markgröningen) in Swabia, which was also described in the text, as we saw earlier. This addition leads us to wonder whether a change was also made in the map in 1527. Since the words "Swabia" and "margt Grieningen" are not inscribed on the one preserved copy of the map it seems reasonable to assume that sheet b, which includes that area, is of the 1525 issue of the map. In the 1530 edition of the *Uslegung*, thirteen more place names were added to the register, but without being indexed, and only two of these, Wismar and Olmnitz, are to be found on Fries's *Carta Marina*.[19] It seems likely that mention of these towns, many of them near Strassburg, was a concession to local interest in the places where the *Carta Marina* and the *Uslegung* were most frequently sold.

Approximately a sixth of the chapters in all three editions tell about foreign places, including America. Grüninger's insistent plea for more information, preferably from merchants, about "faraway lands" suggests that Fries had enough material about Germany, Italy, and the rest of Europe, probably from Waldseemüller's notes. Grüninger wanted news from merchants in Nürnberg, hoped to get some book — the title unspecified — from the bishop of Brixen, and requested a book about the Cape of Good Hope from Hans Koberger. The first edition of the *Uslegung* also contained a full-page map bound with the chapter on America which showed the route of Cadamosto's first voyage, demonstrating Grüninger's desire to give the reader as much material as he had about the discoveries. This map, left out in 1527 and 1530, says that "this was the first voyage during which they looked for new lands, the others will be described in the larger book." This might have led contemporary readers to make vain inquiries at a bookstall; the reader of more than four hundred years later is also puzzled by this reference.

This map in the *Uslegung* of 1525 has Latin names showing southeastern Portugal and Lisbon in the upper right, Madeira to the left, and Palma at the lower or southern border. It is titled "the first table which shows the voyage of Cadamosto to the island of Madeira." [20] Also, the first chapter of the text dealing with America announces that more will be said about Amerigo Vespucci in the other book. There are similar promises in the next chapters, of which the one about England has this sentence: "The deeds which the English kings have committed would be too long to tell because we do not want to describe a *Chronik* here." [21] It is clear that Fries composed the *Uslegung* in the firm belief that a large *Chronica Mundi* would be published as a companion volume to the map, and that his smaller work was precisely what the title says — an interpretation of the map, a guidebook or gazetteer to explain what could be found on it with the help of the other book. He had the *Uslegung* ready by March 12, 1525, but Grüninger did not publish it until fall because the publication of the Ptolemy delayed him and he could not get the maps printed. The last we hear of the *Chronica Mundi* which was never written is in Grüninger's letter to Willibald Pirckheimer after the Ptolemy was published:

DEAR SIR:

I still have a letter from you in which you showed yourself kindly disposed when I wrote your dignity that Martin Waldseemüller had started to describe the itineraria of the whole world for me and that I had ordered woodcuts of many towns and strange people which the *Carta Marina* shows in Latin and German . . . I ask you to kindly help and advise me so that it is not abandoned. I have let it lie around for eight years now and would certainly like to have it put in order with the many new discoveries in it too. [22]

We can surmise Pirckheimer's reaction to this letter, particularly when he looked at the "gift" Grüninger had sent: the new *Carta Marina* in German by Doctor Fries, who was probably known to Pirckheimer as a writer of popular medical tracts in German and only too well known as a poor editor of Ptolemy. Pirckheimer could also read on the map that this same Fries was going to have ready in the near future a little book to accompany the map, God willing. At one time, if we are to believe Grüninger in the letter quoted, Pirckheimer must have written favorably about the project of a book to go with Waldseemüller's map. Pirckheimer was interested in the geography of the newly discovered lands, and the latest reports were more easily obtained in Nürnberg where he lived than in Strassburg.[23] But since Pirckheimer apparently ignored Grüninger's request, the opportunity of publishing a world map by Waldseemüller with a great book by Pirckheimer was now lost. The reference to "the larger book" on the map of Cadamosto's voyage in the *Uslegung* serves as a reminder of an unrealized project in geographic writing in the sixteenth century.

It is certain that Fries used notes by Waldseemüller when he composed the *Uslegung*. He also had a good lead to sources through the names that Waldseemüller had printed on the large shield at the lower left of his map. But we cannot be quite certain whether the many passages which appear in the *Uslegung* literally copied from the German edition of the *Paesi Nuovamente Retrovati* and from Lodovico di Varthema's travels were copied by Fries from the respective books or from excerpts made by Waldseemüller. Some material about European places may date back to the work of Waldseemüller and Ringmann, jointly undertaken for the map of Europe of 1511, and the manual for it, particularly in view of the fact that Grüninger kept both alive through his republications in 1520 and 1527.[24] The chapter about Franconia in the *Uslegung* is similar to the text on the front and verso of the *Tabula Moderna Germaniae* in the Ptolemy of 1522. A Latin sentence from the *Tabula Moderna Germaniae* about the Waldensian sect and the infectious poison spread by the adherents of Huss could be attributed to Waldseemüller. Notes from Waldseemüller must have been used by Fries when he, who was antagonistic to Greece, described Athens as the mother of liberal arts and philosophy and when he treated Greece favorably in the 1522 Ptolemy,[25] in contrast to his own description of Greece in 1525. It is even possible that he found a remark among Waldseemüller's notes which sparked him to write the passage critical of the

Holy Land which aroused so much attention later on in connection with Servetus' trial for heresy. This geographically correct observation of the water problem in Palestine is almost too astute to be Fries's. On the other hand we may hold him responsible for the hostile tone of his description of Judea, since we know the tone of his prognostication *Der Juden Practica* for 1525, mentioned earlier:

This land was ruled by the Jews in times past, and their leader, Moses, has promised it to them by saying he would lead them into a land where honey flows and milk. But if it now has enough water it would be content. Many write of the richness and the fertility of this land. But, truly, it is a despoiled, miserable, infertile country. It would be well nowadays if they would accept the Jews that one would send to their land. Jerusalem is the capital in the middle of this land, a torn dark city with low earthen houses. Onc can still see the temple of Solomon held in honor by the Turks and no Christian may go near it. One can also see the burial place of Christ, the old mountain and the place of his crucifixion as well as the house of Pilate and many others.[26]

Fries's authorship accounts for all the hostile references to Luther, since Waldseemüller died around 1517–1518 and specific anti-Lutheran utterances cannot be expected before the nailing of the ninety-five theses on the church door in Wittenberg in 1517. These references are sometimes veiled; for instance, England had kings which "take a stand for Christianity, so that St. Peter's ship is not quite so lamentably sunk by pirates, and by the current prophet and his clientele. Oh, if we had such a king, it would truly be better than it is now."[27] This goes back to the stand Henry VIII took in 1521, which earned him the title "defender of Faith." It is also a reflection of Grüninger's polemic tract, published, as he once said, because he wanted to make a living (see page 25).[28] Leipzig, briefly described, is said to have been beautiful "before Luther's muse spoiled it with his poetry."[29] The people in Nubia are Christians, "but of the Lutheran type" since they do not believe in the incarnation of Christ.[30] In Poland are various Christians, some of the

Bohemian, some of the Greek type; but "in Cracow and the cities people generally stay with the right church order." [31] This last as well as the reference to Christian heretics in Taurisium and the Wallachians' faith "which is like that of the Greek sect" reflects more of a traditional Roman Catholic point of view than the anti-Lutheranism of the early twenties, and thus could have originated with Waldseemüller. [32]

Very few passages in the *Uslegung* are dated. The remark about the conquest of Rhodes must be by Fries, because of its date; but the phrase inserted after the introductory chapters and before the register must have been copied literally from a note by Waldseemüller. It reads: "This register starts with the letter A, the new land America which twenty-five years ago was unknown and unheard of by anybody." [33] If we assume that Waldseemüller wrote this in 1517 while preparing an index for the *Carta Marina*, "twenty-five years ago" makes sense as the year 1492. If Fries had written this in 1525, it would mean 1500. The reference to Christopher Columbus who "*some short years* ago discovered the islands with cannibals" also sounds a little more plausible as a phrase of Waldseemüller's in 1516 than as one by Fries, who had written about guayac wood from America as early as 1518, put the year 1497 as that of the discovery on a map he made in 1520, and used the dates 1492 and 1497 in his Ptolemy edition of 1522. [34]

Finally, one could postulate that Fries stopped to copy Waldseemüller's notes in the middle of a sentence in the long passage about Amerigo Vespucci, because Waldseemüller's notes end abruptly in the third person and Fries then equally abruptly inserts Vespucci's first-person report: "Americus and his people had now sufficiently observed these people . . . then twenty-two small rafts came toward him on the sea and formed a ring around them and they heard great wondering," immediately continuing: "at *our* looks although *we* gave them many tokens of friendship." [35]

We have enough evidence to conclude that Fries worked with Waldseemüller's notes, but we cannot tell precisely which passages he copied from the notes and which were his own.

On the whole, it is doubtful that an unprepared reader could detect from the book that the writer was a doctor and astrologer. Guayac wood, a pharmaceutical, was mentioned, of course; but only once. There were no references to the geographic origin of remedies, to medical schools in European cities, or to contemporary doctors. Lübeck had a fine hospital, the book said, and in the kingdom of Melli in West Africa salt was used to make medicine.[36] The island of Sardinia had hot springs with healing qualities, and the hot water was also used to tell honest people from thieves because it blinded the guilty when put into their eyes. The herbs which "grow on a mountain near Verona and are widely distributed to aid people's health" could have come to Fries's attention on his journey to Italy, but this information might also have been known to the pharmaceutical trade at large; Fries did not name the herbs. He mentioned only one doctor in the whole book, "the famous physician Thadeum," together with Dante, Petrarca, Leonardo da Vinci, and Accursium, as having contributed to the fame of Florence.[37] If one wants to include the one unfavorable comment about Rome — "where they do not have good water" — as the sort of observation a doctor would make, all specific references to illness, hospitals, remedies, and doctors have now been enumerated.[38] One looks in vain among the countries of Africa for any passage that has the directness of the *Spiegel*, where Fries recommended different treatment for peoples in different countries: "If a Moor comes from his hot land and gets sick in our country the doctor must not only consider the disease but must remember that this Moor has lived in a very hot country and therefore has wider pores through which to perspire." [39]

Astrology, Fries's great love, does not appear in the *Uslegung* any oftener than medicine. All the celestial lore the book offers is presented in the first part, which Fries wrote more independently than the second. He makes no specific reference to astrologers, citing as authorities Strabo's first book, Aristotle and Pliny for winds, Amerigo Vespucci for America, Konrad Celtis for Nürnberg, Titus Livius for Naples, Pomponius (Mela) for Rhodes, and Hieronymus for Worms. Cadamosto and Varthema were not mentioned, although Fries used both extensively in German editions. There is, of course, praise for Ptolemy's "right cosmography" as the general source of information in the first chapter.[40] No other sources are identified by name, let alone by title, and the intent behind the few names mentioned is clear: Fries wanted to be protected by authorities and he considered only the long-established classics safe. He was no longer the young doctor who had written a successful medical book in German for the people, but a man harassed by the cold reception his Ptolemy had got from humanists and by the ridicule of his astrological anti-Lutheran writings. So he closed his *Uslegung* with a plea:

DEAR GRÜNINGER:

In fulfillment of your desire I have endeavored for the embellishment of the Carta Marina to describe the noteworthy lands and cities, as much as I was able, through new relations and writings as well as through experience of others and my own. Please, will you accept this in good grace, and be satisfied with my small talent? And continue — regarding this and other works — to vouch for me and to protect me from the jealous who, after a work is done, want to make it better — if they can.[41]

The *Uslegung* of 1525 was Fries's last book, and the first of three editions which became successively shorter because of the omission of illustrations and in 1530 an abbreviated text. All three editions were printed in gothic minuscule. The first two editions had large carved gothic initials at the beginnings of the nine introductory chapters and simple humanistic type face for initials throughout the descriptive text.[42]

The Book and the Map

For the edition of 1530 eight different kinds of initial were used, ranging from large carved gothic letters and encased decorated letters from Grüninger's children's alphabet to small humanistic type and the same capital letters that were used in the text; this gave the book a careless appearance. The text was in the so-called Upper Rhine German type face, the pagination was incomplete, and roman page numbers and the numbering of the chapters were often faulty.[43] It is impossible to distinguish errors in typesetting from Fries's own errors, nor can it be assumed that he was certain of any correct way of spelling a place name. Some differences among the editions do not justify searching comparisons, since they might well be the result of the sort of typesetter's prank from which the *Spiegel* had suffered.[44] The most significant difference is the abridgment of the third edition by omitting the views of Calicut and Venice and the ten most appealing pictures, and by shortening the descriptions of foreign lands. By and large the 1530 edition of the *Uslegung* reflected less world-mindedness than did the first edition.

Though the register in the *Uslegung* was a convenient tool for the user of the *Carta Marina* in that it helped him to locate some two hundred places, it was the text proper which provided information about Europe and foreign lands, thereby supplementing the numerous legends on the *Carta Marina*. In a convenient alphabetical arrangement Fries described places, countries, and peoples of all parts of the world in a hundred and seventeen chapters that are uneven in both length and quality. Each of the German states received about equal attention, most of it focused on such specific characteristics as Prussia's Order of the German Knights; Bavaria's being ruled by a duke and no longer by a king; Switzerland as a producer of fine milk and cheese; and Austria, Bohemia, Franconia, and Swabia as fertile lands, and, except for Bohemia, producing excellent wines. The people were agreeable in all of these countries, but in Swabia they were "most industrious and inclined to travel far." There were no chapters for Germany as a whole, or for Alsace or Lorraine; but Fries described Burgundy as "fertile and useful" wherefore "many wars were fought over this little country, although according to natural rights [*natürlichen rechten*] it belonged to the praiseworthy King of France" — one of the earliest references to natural rights regarding boundaries in political geography. Fries was antagonistic to neo-Grecism and consequently to Greece, but his personal experiences, or possibly his adherence to the established church, made him give Italy and Rome the two longest paragraphs of any European country:

Italy is a country that Europe may well be proud of. Say what you will about all countries and the whole world, nothing can compare with Italy! The air is good and mild. The soil is fertile and produces the noblest wines, grain, olive oil, pomegranates, oranges, lemons, melons, cantaloupes, figs, almonds, and all kinds of fruit from trees. It also has meadows, waters, fish, cattle, small and big game, and all imaginable resources. In addition, this country has the best harbors, where many imports are unloaded. The people in this country know much, have good manners and customs. If you look for masters in all kinds of art you won't find them anywhere else than in Italy, be it in theology, in both laws, liberal arts, philosophy, statesmanship, or in crafts which are highly regarded. What am I to say of the German humanists or others who think nobody is their equal with respect to the Latin or Greek language? Truly, a young girl in Italy would surpass them! Equally, if you desire generally useful administration of justice look for it only in Italy. If you look for beautiful and well built castles and palaces you will find them only in Italy! This country does not lack any material thing, it has gold, silver, ores, and hot springs for various illnesses. A wonderful people — tall men and still more beautiful women.[45]

Fries had visited Verona, Bologna, Florence, and Siena en route to Rome from the north. The difference in his descriptions is revealed by the chapters about Genoa (Janus) and Siena (Senis), which are exactly the same length, eleven printed lines:

Janus, a famous city on the Ligurian Sea, built by King Jano. This is a port and warehouse town in Liguria. It developed very much through conquest, power, and strength of navigation. It almost surpasses all other Italian towns in high buildings and all sorts of decorations.

Senis, the city in Italy, lies on a beautiful hill which has wonderful buildings, a university, and a royal palace. This city is spacious and kept free with the help of towers and ramparts. Its citizens have very nice manners and are not uncouth or impolite. The soil around it is very fertile and everything is found in abundance there.

Fries obviously had visited Siena but not Genoa.

Some European countries, he mentioned, were noted for their mineral resources, such as England and Spain, and the latter's fertility, like that of Hungary and Portugal, was praised in terms of the wine and grain it produced. The people of Ireland and Poland were "uncouth and rustic"; nor did the Wallachians, Russians, Albanians, or Hungarians find favor with Fries, though the French did.[46] The climate of Denmark and treeless Scotland, together with their quarrelsome inhabitants, made these countries sound unattractive also. The only short description of a European country from an economic point of view was that of Lithuania:

Lithuania is a wide land bordering Poland, full of forests. It is not easy to get to this country during summer. But during the winter season one travels there on sleighs over the frozen sea. Thus the merchants journey to Lithuania in winter and take along food for many days, since they find no hostels along this route. Most Lithuanian commerce deals with furs, mink, Siberian squirrels, and other pelts.[47]

Remarks about the many apiaries in Poland and the salt mines in Portugal, where one need not obtain salt by evaporation, represented the only other specific information about economic geography.

For Corsica, only the origin of its name was reported, and for Sardinia, the name and its hot springs. In the thirty Orchades (Orkney) islands were sandy wastes without woods where lived poor and pious people who ate fish and lived in reed houses: "There is not much that is strange and pretty one can write about them. For these islands lie very close to the location where the cold is so great that one does not want to live there any more. It is only five days' travel to the frozen sea. You can well imagine what good these islands are." [48]

It was obviously much better to live in cities, and Europe emerges as a continent of cities in Fries's *Uslegung*, many of them receiving historical rather than geographical treatment. Strassburg was accorded more space than other German cities, Leipzig by far the least: it was beautiful but spoiled for Fries by Luther. The merry city of Vienna was apparently described from personal experience, as were details about the cathedrals in Speyer and Ulm and the castle and university of Prague. Churches were the only important features of Würzburg and Munich; fortifications distinguished Nürnberg and Cracow, and Trier and Augsburg were famous for relics and historical legends. The origin of the names of the cities of Bamberg, Cologne, Buda, Metz, and Erfurt, the wars in the history of Worms, and the establishment by Charlemagne of a bishop's seat at Magdeburg Fries apparently assumed were of greater interest to readers than geographical descriptions.

Geographically significant details make the reading about some cities more interesting: Salzburg, with its hills and river meadows, where wine, hay, fowl, game, and fish came from, and which played a role as a thoroughfare for merchants journeying to Italy; and the wooden bridge with twenty-four arches across the Moldau at Prague. Special mention was made of the street plans of Breslau, where houses were well aligned "so that no house takes away the view from the next," and of Lübeck, where streets extending from a central elevation washed waste away so that the city was very clean. Of Frankfurt, where the two parts of the town were connected by a sturdy stone bridge over the Main, Fries would not omit mentioning that "there lived many Jews in this town who had their own street." [49] The chapter on the small but well-built city of Constance featured Lake Constance, inlet and outlet for the Rhine, described as seven miles long with very clear water which ran over stony ground and was full of fish.[50]

Thus Fries's "personal new experience," mentioned in his concluding note to Grüninger in the *Uslegung,* was reflected only incidentally regarding German cities and then only in one really geographic description, that of Strassburg. His treatment of Italian cities, with the exception of Genoa, reflected the fact that he had not only seen but loved them, most of all Rome:

Rome, a city famous all over the whole world, situated on the river Tiber, was named after Romulus who built it. The Tiber flows from the north into the city and leaves it toward the south in the direction of Ostia. On the right bank the city has two mountains, the Vatican and Janiculum. On the left bank the city includes seven hills named Capitoline, Aventine, Palatine, Caelian, Esquiline, Viminal, and Quirinal. Every one of these hills has its buildings, houses, and churches. This city is wonderfully built up with great mansions and castles. The city is well protected by towers and walls. This is the seat of the highest priest of the Christians.

What shall I say about Rome? Read all that you can find about all cities in the world, be it about gold, silver, gems, precious clothes, beautiful buildings, persons learned in all arts and crafts, about great noblemen and poor servants, fine horses and donkeys — you find it all in Rome in abundance. Only good water — of that they have little. If I wanted to describe the churches in Rome I would have to write a special book. The same goes for its sacred places. But this is not appropriate now, therefore I have said enough of Rome at this time.[51]

The religious partiality which Fries allowed to appear in most of the *Uslegung* makes the printing of three editions during the five years when the Reformation reached its height in Strassburg and surrounding cities all the more remarkable.

Among Europe's world ports in the age of discovery, Antwerp, Venice, and Lisbon were treated in a manner that might be considered adequate for the gazetteer that the *Uslegung* claimed to be. Ships "loaded with silk, clothes, gold, spices, brazilwood, strange animals and birds, various fish, and many people from Portugal, Castile, England, Venice, and Barbaria" came to Antwerp and brought similar cargo to Lisbon, where "strange people were being sold for small sums." [52] Such ancient cities as Alexandria, Constantinople, and Heliopolis were described in the traditional manner, while Cairo was reported to be under the control of the Saracens now and a great center of commerce from Calicut, India, and Arabia. The chapters about Damascus, Mecca, and Medina were comparatively long and even in spelling based on the 1515 German translation of Varthema's travels. [53] In spite of the great interest of Europeans in the Turkish menace, Fries's chapter on Turkey was relatively short and told only about Mohammed and the Islamic interpretation of the birth of Christ. [54]

Stereotyped and scanty as much of the information which readers of 1525 could get from the *Uslegung* may appear, it is still revealing. The stress on fertile or infertile soils in the countries or in the immediate environment of cities; the mention of the production of wine and the availability of fish and game; the repeated details about bridges, sites of castles relative to cities, and the latter's fortifications were all interesting to citizens of German towns, particularly Strassburgers. Site is an important geographic fact and a river which furnished fish but no impediment to travel because it was conveniently bridged was an important asset to a city. Fortifications were as important to urban dwellers during the period of Peasants' War and the Turkish menace as urban renewal is to Americans of our time. The height of churches with their location, relics, and the towers from which their signals announced events, curfews, or hours of prayer, the extent of cities by width and the available space into which citizens, tradespeople, and migrants crowded during daytime — all these were real aspects which determined the nature of urban life for a Strassburger in 1525. On the other hand, the *Carta Marina* and the *Uslegung* gave no population statistics except for Mecca, "a very beautiful town which has almost six thousand hearths with houses worth about 3–4,000 ducats." The *Uslegung*, designed as a companion to the *Carta Marina*, which had many legends for faraway countries, devoted about half of its approximately twenty-seven hundred lines to cities and countries outside Europe in the editions of 1525 and 1527.

In the second edition, Cadamosto's map and six woodcut pictures were missing, but an eagle on the title page, designed by Hans Baldung Grien, was a decorative addition.[55] Two folded double-page illustrations of Calicut and Venice and four more woodcuts were left out of the edition of 1530, so that only four woodcut illustrations, all looking worn from long usage, accompanied this last German edition, which had the somewhat overused cannibal scene on its title page. All but one of all the pictures showed foreign countries and thus were an integral part of the information the *Uslegung* imparted about the non-European world. The reader's view of the world was as much affected by them as by the text; the contribution of Grüninger's engravers to the geographic education of the reader deserves more than passing notice.

Altogether, Grüninger had twenty-three different woodcut pictures in the two Ptolemy editions of 1522 and 1525 and the *Uslegung* of 1525. No new woodcut was added to the *Uslegung* after 1525. All of the wood blocks were new in 1522 and still made excellent prints in the *Uslegung*, although they were probably used at least fifteen hundred times, assuming conservatively that each edition was printed in five hundred copies. All are very similar and about equally large, varying between 13 by 6 to 14 by 10.2 centimeters. One, a scene with figures under trees by the water in a violent dance and blowing a long horn, was of outstanding artistic quality. This is on the front page of the Tabula Moderna Indiae Orientalis in the Ptolemy of 1522, and was not used again in the *Uslegung*; the lover of woodcuts must regret this omission.

All fourteen woodcut illustrations in the *Uslegung* were designed and cut by the same hands or "school." A well-drawn scene of Columbus by the shore (13.5 by 9.2 centimeters), which was discussed in connection with the distinctive sheet of the Tabula Terre Novae in the Ptolemy of 1522, appeared in the *Uslegung* to illustrate the chapter about Spagnola. The text told how the ship ran aground offshore, how "Christoff Dauber" sent men in small boats to meet the natives, how these fled but left behind a woman to whom the sailors gave European clothes. Thereupon the natives became friendly and swam around between the boat and the shore and gifts were exchanged. Picture and text complement each other nicely.

The island of Samotra, about which little more could be learned from the map than that it presented a location problem in Ptolemy and Solinus, was illustrated in the text. This delightful woodcut of 13.2 by 9.2 centimeters shows a large elephant and a woman with a strong healthy infant on her left arm. Another boy is grimacing at her from the branch of a tree which he has just climbed and she is obviously warning a third child not to swing too violently on the trunk of a patient elephant. Though the woman's lack of clothing set her aside from German mothers of 1525, the humor of the scene underlines its validity in the history of mankind: women minding three boys of preschool age out-of-doors with animals around always had and always will have a trying task, be it in Samotra, where they have elephants, or in Strassburg, where they have horses. According to the text, many of the world's greatest elephants were in Samotra, and its people were not very skillful but were kind to strangers. Here all sorts of spices but not many other edible products could be found and "fine justice" was administered.

The Book and the Map

In the 1525 edition, one large and two smaller animals with spotted hides illustrate the account of Zeyla in Africa, which had "unbelievably many great and strange animals, leopards and elephants" and also "a great deal of gold and many persons who had been conquered in Prester John's land, taken prisoner and led away so that they were sold into all lands."

Strange animals appeared also on the pictures for Cuba and Brazil. The large, writhing body of a great snake covered most of the picture for Cuba, where Columbus's men had found such snakes even tied to trees by natives who wanted them for food. A Cuban village with church steeple, gabled houses, smoke from a chimney, and a ruined castle in the background were unmistakably Alsatian and thus reassuringly familiar to a Strassburger. Brazil was illustrated by unicorns, at which two naked natives, armed with bow, arrows, and shields, gazed warily, under trees that looked very much like the gnarled conifers on the heights of the Vosges. People in Prasilia were "simple like cattle," went naked, and lived on fruit and herbs because there were few fish, some wondrous animals, and parrots, which the studious reader could perhaps recognize as the *papagalli* of *Prisilia* on the map. Gold and pearls could be got from there, but the people had no iron for axes and knives and cut their wood with tools of stone. A hopeful note was added: "But now the land grows several crops and the people have learned to dress themselves in animal hides and birds' feathers since the King of Portugal occupied the land with his people which, day by day, have taught those inhabitants how to lead a different life."

The powerful rulers of strange countries were not described as if they were eager to learn much, but in a rather respectful way. Prester John was shown in the center of a hall on a throne with rows of dogs at each side and a mass of soldiers with lances. The King of Pego in India liked to sit outside in front of his pavilion and was scantily dressed because of the great heat. The fence and garden gate did not look very different from those in the countryside around Strassburg, but there was a palm tree in the otherwise Alsatian-looking landscape. Fries found it "impossible to describe" the immense riches of brazilwood, sandalwood, cotton, silk, gold, and rubies in Pego.

The King of Fesa also sat outside, but in front of his house, not a pavilion, perhaps because he was reported to have a "well-built capital city." He and his people dressed in clean white linen and wore gold and pearls. They were Mohammedans and the picture therefore had a round building in the rear reminiscent of the city symbols on the map for Mecca and Medina. Since nobody would approach the king except on his knees, a man knelt in front of him. It looked as if grain had been spread at the base of the throne. The text said that this land yielded good crops and from each grain put into the soil one would harvest a hundred.

In Narsinga the king was being served in the open by two skillful and speedy waiters with a set of covered trays and a goblet of wine. Trees and the corner of a thatched roof over the house from which these came made this look like a picnic rather than a royal occasion. But the king was reported to have an entourage of six thousand horses and though he, like the King of Calicut, prayed to the devil, he was also a friend of Christians and his land was as safe for travel as the land around Calicut.[56]

For Murfuli the woodcut illustrates a human aspect of a curious old legend about diamonds which the rain may wash down from the hills, thus allowing them to be found at the bottom of steep mountains or clinging to the meat brought up by eagles. They could not always catch the meat as it was thrown to them, and had to pick it out of the abyss. On the woodcut the naked natives have glued diamonds to their bodies and look spotted. Most German city dwellers of 1525, who were used to looking at woodcuts, probably had to read the story before they understood why these two naked spotted men and the woman with her child on her back looked happy and hale in the deep forest. These were not lepers or people afflicted with advanced gallic disease and therefore chased into the forest, as was the custom before progressive cities like Strassburg established special hospitals for them (contemporary woodcut illustrations of this tragic aspect of life in Germany of the second decade of the sixteenth century looked strikingly similar). The *Uslegung* said that people in Murfuli had wine, meat, and rice but had to give the largest diamonds to their masters.

The strange and unfamiliar are less pleasantly portrayed on the remaining pictures. One of five people in a boat was shooting poisoned arrows into the air around the island of Cape Verde, which was very beautiful and had two mountains, according to the text. This geographic detail was probably the reason for the rocky island in the background. None of the houses that were reported near the shore was shown on the picture. Pigmies lived in corral-like compartments constructed of brush and branches in a field watched over by a European-style castle on a hill in an unmistakably Upper Rhine landscape. The old story that the pigmies must burn their white pepper so that vermin would not spoil it was about all that was told about the desert of India "through which it is almost impossible to travel."

Only two of the fourteen pictures could inspire terror: dog-headed men on the island of the cannibals, which Columbus had discovered, prepare human cuts on a butcher's block to illustrate the chapter on cannibals, and the reader is told that the people liked this food and often sailed to other islands to bring home their prey. More unpleasant yet is the scene in Java where a person who had been declared incurably sick and therefore killed is now put above a fire, presumably to be roasted.

Two larger folding pictures of the waterfronts of Venice and Calicut were totally different from the other illustrations because they put little emphasis on human beings and seem to have been done by another hand. Venice was portrayed as a busy port with numerous gondolas at its wharves, and over the whole city the spire of St. Mark's stood dominant. An interesting detail is the word *Germanum* on one of the piers, possibly marking a new factory for German merchants replacing the Fondaco, the old German merchants' club in Venice, which had burned; but the accompanying text sheds no light on the role of German merchants in Venice.[57] Calicut, the emporium of the east, with its tall buildings, round watchtowers, gabled houses, and arched gates, looked different from familiar European cities only in that an elephant strolled its streets and palm trees gave it a tropical aspect.

Thus the *Uslegung*'s map and fifteen of the sixteen pictorial illustrations were concerned with foreign countries that had become important through recent discoveries. All sixteen pictures had text complementing them so that they could be understood only if the book was read. The designer must have known details from the text in order to put them in the illustrations. Since we know that Grüninger had most of the illustrations ready before either he or Fries had thought of a guidebook, it is apparent that appropriate textual descriptions were on hand, with the pictures, when Fries composed the *Uslegung*. Since Grüninger tried very hard to get material about Lisbon while Fries was redrawing the *Carta Marina*, it is even possible that the illustration of Venice was a substitute for one of Lisbon. Calicut and Lisbon were the two places everybody who had heard about Portuguese trade thought of, and the chapter about Calicut in the *Uslegung* begins typically: "Calicut, the noteworthy city of commerce, is greater than Lisbon."[58]

The artistic quality of the pictures in the *Uslegung* was higher than that of the illustrations on the *Carta Marina*, except for the figure of King Emanuel and the borders on the *Carta Marina*. The pictures are without monogram, and Paul Kristeller's evaluation of them as a group with a specific Grüninger style created by the craftsmen who worked only for him shortly before 1520 is the most plausible. At least one of these *formenschneider* must have returned to Grüninger's workshop when the *Carta Marina* was engraved again in 1524 and 1525.

If Grüninger or Fries could have secured or had been willing to use more recent newsletters, the text in the *Uslegung* of 1525 could have reflected such world events as Magellan's journey. But it takes time for the results of explorations to become as much a part of general knowledge as were medieval and ancient legends in Fries's time. Fries hesitated to repeat information from sources that were not authoritative, and he was not like Waldseemüller, who made enthusiastic use of Vespucci's travels when he wrote his *Cosmographia Introductio* as a schoolbook in 1507. Fries did not even decide what part Christopher Columbus and Amerigo Vespucci had played in the discovery of America.[59] The contradictions in his publications did not concern Grüninger either. After Waldseemüller was no longer willing to call the new lands "America" on his *Carta Marina* in 1516, Grüninger printed his first Ptolemy, which contained Fries's *Orbis Typus* with the name "America" and Waldseemüller's Terre Novae without it, accompanied by text which credited Columbus with the discovery of the New World. Grüninger could not read the Latin of his Ptolemy. But in 1525 Fries did nothing to clarify the two versions for German readers and for Grüninger. At best, they now could believe, according to the *Uslegung*, that "Christoff Dauber" had discovered Spagnola and that "Americus Vesputius" had discovered the fourth part of the world. The *Carta Marina* also told of Columbus as the discoverer of Spagnola and of Castilians and Portuguese as the discoverers of what later on would be called South America, though the Strassburger in 1525 could call it Terra Nova, Terra Parias, Terra Cannibalorum, Prasilia (spelled in one of three ways), or Terra Papagalli.[60]

But the reader in Strassburg conceived of all countries as kingdoms and was probably less interested in names than in the foreign kings —

what they ate, how they were served, how many wives they had, how many jewels were in their crowns, how they went into battle, what gifts they demanded from their subjects. The reader was expected to be interested most of all in what was *seltsam und wunderbarlich*, strange and wondrous.

At a time when world geography implied reconciling Ptolemy, Columbus, Amerigo Vespucci, and Varthema, Fries, in presenting the strange and wondrous, refrained from the sensationalism of a Sir John Mandeville. Grüninger, the major partner in the enterprise of producing a popular world map with a guidebook, also showed restraint regarding the depiction of the monstrosities shown by many woodcut illustrations in contemporary books, including the great folio volume of Hartman Schedel's *Nürnberg Chronicle* of 1493, and Sebastian Münster's *Cosmographia* of 1544. Münster's immensely popular work served general geographic education in Germany for nearly a hundred years and it was the renowned cosmographer Münster in 1544 not Fries in 1525 who repeated the tale of the birth of a child with two heads which supposedly had occurred near Worms in 1495. Otherwise, both Fries and Münster not only applied their different talents to the same task, a popular geography of the world, but shared an allegiance to Ptolemy, whom each had edited before he undertook his popular book in German.[61] Fries's *Carta Marina* and *Uslegung* represented a first step toward popular geographic education and though he approached the task from the same ethnocentric point of view as most contemporary geographers, he also showed considerable kindness and a sense of human dignity. In this Grüninger supported him and emerges as the great printer of wall maps for mass distribution. Grüninger's press was an important force in the spreading of new geographic knowledge, though not so important as he would have liked, since he was frustrated in his desire to publish a *Chronica Mundi* for the *Carta Marina*.

The Book and the Map

The *Carta Marina* and *Uslegung* reflected the coincidence of the age of the discovery with the humanistic revival of Greek and Latin, that is, the scholarly endeavor to validate Ptolemy. While Portuguese and other sailors risked their lives year after year to chart new courses and shorelines, many cosmographers in Europe studied the New World only after making a great detour through the world of Ptolemy.[62] Some undertook the task of translating Ptolemy from original manuscripts, a work which inspires the deepest respect.[63] Others, among them Waldseemüller, used one of Ptolemy's projections and located on it the places in the known world as accurately as possible, going beyond Ptolemy. The cosmographers at Nürnberg formed a school of mathematical geography and the cosmographers of St. Dié and Strassburg began to tell stories about the various places and peoples. The technique of doing this by means of legends on the map itself made fewer illustrations necessary and covered blank spaces which would have detracted from a map's appeal to the wider public. So the *Carta Marina* was one of the sixteenth-century maps which imparted information in three ways — through symbols and names, legends, and pictures.[64]

Scholars of Latin may have found the inscriptions wanting in precision, and merchants may not have found much new information about commercial opportunities; but the *Carta Marina*, though it had no projection, was a plane map with the advantages for untrained viewers which have made Mercator's projection popular to this day. Orientation as to cardinal directions is consistent; north and south, east and west everywhere appear as up and down, right and left, respectively. Thus the *Carta Marina* and the *Uslegung*, with the latter's accurate location numbers in the register, offered people in southwestern Germany a comparatively early opportunity to take a faltering step toward gaining a new view of the world. But "an old world view does not dissolve overnight."[65] Since the step was taken during a time when many questions were vainly addressed to the authority of Ptolemy when they should have been answered by direct observation and improved measurement, confusion reigned and was compounded by mapmakers' poor training, lack of experience, erroneous sources of information, and vivid imaginations. Tradition and authority meant hindrance to some scholars, security to others. After the discoveries, a Strassburger would eventually have to recognize that the world included another continent and roughly twice as much area as had been assumed for nearly two thousand years to exist. It would take many decades to shake off the restraints of earlier learning and many centuries to recognize the fallacies of ethnocentrism. Grüninger, whose highly productive publishing house helped to broadcast to large numbers of German people much that was new and appeared strange and a great deal that was familiar since it was confirmed by old beliefs, and Fries, the author and map designer who was called upon to perpetuate Waldseemüller's heritage, both deserve recognition for their role in the beginnings of geographic education for the people. The study of the *Carta Marina* and the *Uslegung* also reveals that Martin Waldseemüller, best known for his *Cosmographia Introductio*, a 1507 globe design and wall map, exerted a strong influence on popular geographic knowledge until 1530 through Grüninger's press, and that Johannes Grüninger, with his nearly a hundred thousand sheets of woodcut maps, was the foremost printer of wall maps in Germany during the first three decades of the sixteenth century.

NOTES

STRASSBURG IN 1525

[1] *Uslegung der Mercarthen oder Cartha Marina Darin man sehen mag wa einer in der Welt sey vnd wa ein ietlich Land Wasser vnd Stat gelegen ist. Das als in den büchlin zefinden.* Getruckt zū Strassburg von Johannes Grieninger und vollendet uff unser Lieben Frawen abent der geburt. Im. Jar 1.5.2.5., fol. Bii. The second edition of 1527 is shorter in several places, and the comment on Strassburg stops with "That is why the city is called Strassburg." The third edition of 1530 also stops here and has a slightly different title: *Underweisung vnd vszlegunge Der Cartha Marina oder die mercarten Darin man sehen mag wa einer in der welt sy vnd wa ein ytlich land wasser und stet ligen als in de büchlin angezögt vnd in der charten zusehen.* The best collation of all three editions is found in Walther Ruge, "Älteres kartographisches Material in deutschen Bibliotheken," *Nachrichten von der Königlichen Gesellschaft der Wissenschaften zu Göttingen. Philologisch-historische Klasse. 1916. Beiheft* (1916), pp. 121–23. Strassburg was called Argentoratum in Latin; Fries called it Argentina, shortened to "argen" on the map.

[2] "Zur Geschichte des Strassburger Buchdrucks und Buchhandels," in *Archiv für Geschichte des Deutschen Buchhandels,* ed. by the Historische Kommission of the Börsenverein Deutscher Buchhändler, V (1880), pp. 6–7 and 15–16, lists twenty-nine printers in Strassburg before 1500 and fifty-nine in the sixteenth century.

[3] This description is largely based on the following: comments in Fries's *Uslegung;* Jean-Frédéric Hermann, *Notices Historiques, Statistiques et Littéraires sur la Ville de Strasbourg* (2 vols.; Strasbourg, 1817–1819), vols. I and II *passim;* Franklin L. Ford, *Strasbourg in Transition, 1648–1679* (Cambridge, Mass., 1958), Chapter I; Rodolphe E. Reuss, *Histoire de Strasbourg Depuis ses Origines Jusqu'à nos Jours* (Paris, 1922), Book One, Chapter XIV; Book Two, Chapters I–IV. According to Hermann, *Notices Historiques,* I, 20–21, the foundation dates from 1077, the main aisle from 1275, and the tower was begun in 1277.

[4] For routes taken particularly by carriers of letters and books in the book trade of the time, see Friedrich Kapp, *Geschichte des Deutschen Buchhandels bis in das siebzehnte Jahrhundert,* Vol. I of the series *Geschichte des Deutschen Buchhandels,* ed. by the Historische Kommission of the Börsenverein Deutscher Buchhändler (4 vols.; Leipzig, 1886–1913), pp. 381, 448, 449, 460, 461 (hereafter cited as Kapp, *Deutscher Buchhandel).*

[5] Fries, *Uslegung*, Chapter 19, p. x, "Basel," in all three editions — 1525, 1527, and 1530.

[6] *Ibid.*, Chapter 32, "Frankfurt," in 1525 edition, p. xi; Chapter 43 in 1527 and 1530 editions. An informative but undocumented description of the connections between Strassburg and Frankfurt is to be found in Alexander Dietz, "Strassburg und Frankfurt a.M. Eine Städtefreundschaft," in *Elsass-Lothringisches Jahrbuch*, I (1922), pp. 49–67.

[7] One of the best documented histories is Günther Franz, *Der deutsche Bauernkrieg* (Munich and Berlin, 1933); see pp. 228–43; Reuss, *Histoire de Strasbourg*, pp. 124–28 are less accurate in detail; for instance, on p. 127 he reports twenty thousand slain on May 16, 1525, near Zabern. Franz, *Der deutsche Bauernkrieg*, p. 240, lists four different figures with their sources and settles for "about 18,000" victims.

[8] Karl Theodor Eheberg, "Strassburg's Bevölkerungszahl seit dem Ende des 15. Jahrhunderts bis zur Gegenwart," *Jahrbücher für Nationalökonomie und Statistik*, XLI (1883), pp. 297–314; XLII (1884), pp. 413–30, concludes that between 1473 and 1477 the city had 20,722 residents or 26,198 *Ortsansässige*, when the bailiwicks directly bordering the city are included. In Vol. XLII, pp. 414–15, he cites Gustav Schmoller's figures of 30,000 inhabitants in Strassburg for 1537 on the assumption that a record of 3,698 burghers and guild members in that year represents a family of five each and that a certain number of people without citizen's status must be added. On the basis of lists of deaths and births between 1460 and 1560 Eheberg finds figures of 28,000 city residents and 30,000 when transients are included plausible in 1560. Strassburg increased its population by an eighth during that hundred years, which is very high in view of the checks at work — epidemics, wars, and famines. Hermann, *Notices Historiques*, II, 87, notes 16,000 deaths in Strassburg in 1449.

[9] Hermann, *Notices Historiques*, I, 43, lists the following: the village of Königshofen, 1351 (destroyed 1392), castle Herrenstein near Neuweiler at the foot of the Vosges; the villages of Illkirch, Graffenstade, Illwickersheim in 1418; the village of Niederhausbergen, 1498; castle Wasslenheim in 1496, and its village of Schiltigheim in 1501; Adelshofen in 1502; the villages of Ittenheim and Handschuhheim in 1507.

[10] Hermann, *Notices Historiques*, I, 44–45, says that the great hospital in 1316 was outside the city walls because of the danger of contagion, but was transferred back into the city in 1392. Another hospital was founded between 1370 and 1380 on the Grüne Insel, but we cannot be sure whether it still existed in 1525. Hermann also notes the existence of a hospital named for St. Barbara, an institution for needy transients founded in 1350 and ultimately transferred to the St. Augustine convent after its secularization in 1530. Here 1,600 persons are reported to have stayed during 1530, and 41,058 overnight transients were reported for 1586. See also Eheberg, *Jahrbücher für Nationalökonomie*, XLI, p. 416. The Blatternhaus, a hospital for persons with syphilis, was established in Strassburg

Notes

by the courageous Gaspar Hofmeister in 1502 or 1503, the disease having first appeared in the city about 1495. This hospital was moved to an isle in the Ill River outside the city walls in 1520 (Hermann, *Notices Historiques*, I, p. 157). The city hall or Pfaltz was built in 1321, the mint in 1508, the Pfennigthurm in 1331, the toll house in 1358, the granaries in 1440. See also Otto Winckelmann, "Vom Fürsorgewesen im alten Strassburg," *Elsass-Lothringisches Jahrbuch*, I, pp. 44–48.

[11] Grüninger's house was in the Schlauchgasse, according to the tradition of the firm of Paul Heitz, which still occupies the site. François Ritter, *Histoire de l'Imprimerie Alsacienne au XVe et XVIe Siècles* (Strassburg and Paris, 1955) (Publication de l'Institut des Hautes Études Alsaciennes, Tome XIV), p. 82, locates it at 2 quai du Sable.

[12] The most comprehensive reproduction of woodcuts of this period, many of them from the workshops of Strassburg printers, taken from books, broadsides, playing cards, and separate illustrations, is probably Eugen Diederichs' atlas, *Deutsches Leben der Vergangenheit in Bildern* (2 vols.; Jena, 1908), I, which contains 912 illustrations.

[13] Ford, *Strasbourg in Transition*, pp. 4–5, 10–15, gives a good brief description of the town's government.

[14] Some aspects of this voting are controversial; see Hermann, *Notices Historiques*, I, pp. 54–55, and Reuss, *Histoire de Strasbourg*, p. 122.

[15] Reuss, *Histoire de Strasbourg*, p. 121. The detailed presentation of a great array of facts, events, and personalities is reassuringly concordant in Reuss and Hermann. Contrast a little reader for children, Christian Pfister, *Lectures Alsaciennes*, 3rd ed. (Paris, 1917), published at a time when nationalist feelings ran high, in which the Reformation received scant attention.

[16] Oskar von Hase, *Die Koberger*, 2nd ed. (Leipzig, 1885), in a section entitled "Briefbuch," No. 110 (hereafter references to such letters will be cited as Hase, *Koberger*, "Briefbuch").

JOHANNES GRÜNINGER

[1] Translated from the 1525 edition, p. 1: Gunstiger lieber Grüninger/als ir mich gepeten vor etlicher zeyt die Merkarten in ein kleinere form (eim jetlichen zütetiger/auch in mercklichern verstand/dan sye bitz her gewesen) zü bringen/ had ich eüwerem begeren/von wegen lang geübter früntschafft/mit fügen nit mögen zu wider sein. *Meerkarte* — modern German for Carta Marina — means a world map which shows the oceans. The quotation is the same in the 1527 and 1530 editions.

[2] A short biography of Grüninger is found in Charles G. A. Schmidt, *Jean Grüninger*, 2nd ed. (Strassburg, 1894), which contains a list of 254 thoroughly collated publications by Grüninger. Among shorter essays the following contain good illustrative and documentary material: Werner Cohn, *Einblattdrucke der*

Strassburger Druckerei Johannes Grüninger (Strassburg, 1937); Karl Sudhoff, "Die Herkunft des Strassburger Druckers Johannes Grüninger," *Zeitschrift für Bücherfreunde*, Jahrgang 4 (1900/1901), pp. 440–41; Karl Sudhoff, "Ein Kapitel aus der Geschichte der Setzerwillkur im XVI. Jahrhundert," in *Zeitschrift für Bücherfreunde*, 1902/1903, pp. 79–81 (my source was *Ausgewählte Abhandlungen von Karl Sudhoff*, which makes up Vol. 21 (1929) of *Archiv für Geschichte der Medizin*, pp. 117–20, hereafter cited as *Abhandlungen von Sudhoff*); Robert G. C. Proctor, "Marcus Reinhard and Johann Grüninger," *Bibliographical Essays* (London, 1905), pp. 19–38; Ernst Hermann Voulliéme, *Die Deutschen Drucker des Fünfzehnten Jahrhunderts*, 2nd ed. (Berlin, 1922), pp. 153–56. Ritter, *Histoire de l'Imprimerie Alsacienne*, p. 82, lists further essays about Grüninger.

³ The name of Grüninger also appears as Greninger, Grieninger, Greininger, Groninger, Groininger, and Gürninger in publications from his press. The otherwise identical dedication and preface in 1527 has Grieninger, and in 1530 Grienynger.

⁴ Publications by Grüninger of March 20, 1489, and July 3, 1490, imprinted Johannis and Johannes Reynardi, and of March 4, 1494, imprinted Johannem dictum Reinhart de grunyngen, give us a clue to his birthplace. It is supported by the inclusion of a paragraph on Mark-gröningen in Swabia in the 1527 (fol. C verso) and 1530 (fol. Cij recto) editions of the *Uslegung* with details about a family of Niclas Reim. Fries did not include this paragraph in the edition of 1525. It was added after he had left Strassburg, possibly at Grüninger's suggestion. Further examples of early spellings of Reinhard are to be found in Proctor, *Bibliographical Essays*, p. 20.

⁵ "Item Hans Grünynger, der trucker, hat das burgreht koufft uff mittwoch nach sant Michelstag und will dienen zur steltzen," listed in Charles Wittmer and J. Charles Meyer, *Le Livre de Bourgeoisie de la Ville de Strasbourg, 1440–1530* (3 vols.; Strassburg and Zürich, 1948–1961), I, p. 390.

⁶ Hans H. J. Meyer, "Die Strassburger Goldschmiedezunft von ihrem Entstehen bis 1681," in *Staats- und Sozialwissenschaftliche Forschungen*, Gustav Schmoller, ed., III, Heft 12 (1881), p. 79. See also *Archiv für Geschichte des Deutschen Buchhandels*, V, p. 14.

⁷ See Arthur M. Hind, *An Introduction to a History of Woodcut* (2 vols.; Boston and New York, 1935), II, 344. Gilbert R. Redgrave, "The Illustrated Books of Sebastian Brandt," in *Bibliographica* II (1896), p. 56, calls the Vergil of 1502 "one of the most wonderful illustrated books ever produced." Charles G. A. Schmidt, *Zur Geschichte der ältesten Bibliotheken und der ersten Buchdrucker zu Strassburg* (Strassburg, 1882), p. 113, considers the *Margarita Martiniana* "one of the most beautiful books of the time." On p. 116 Schmidt records information about the few occasions when Grüninger printed for publishers in Speyer, Augsburg, and Nürnberg. The agreement between Grüninger and Hans Schonsperger of Augsburg, however, does not seem to have become a reality. See Freiherr Schenk zu Schweinsberg, "Vertrag zwischen Johannes Grüninger, Buch-

Notes

drucker zu Strassburg, und Hans Schonsperger, Bürger zu Augsburg, . . . 24 März 1502," *Neuer Anzeiger für Bibliographie und Bibliothekwissenschaft*, Jahrgang 1877, pp. 350–51. I agree with the editorial comments by the historical committee of the Börsenverein Deutscher Buchhändler in *Archiv für Geschichte des Deutschen Buchhandels*, V, pp. 1–45: it is not feasible to distinguish sharply between publishers and printers during this period, because they were one or the other or both during one lifetime.

[8] To Schmidt's list of sixty publications in Grüninger's biography of 1892, four listed by Hind can be added for the period 1484–1502. No compilation of all titles which can be added to Schmidt's list of eighty years ago is intended here. The three periods in Grüninger's publications overlap to some degree, certainly with respect to reprints and to the use of the same wood blocks for illustrations.

[9] For the role of correctors, the renumeration of authors, and the pressure of time which led to increasingly careless printing everywhere, see Kapp, *Deutscher Buchhandel*, pp. 308–17. The most famous protest against the haste with which printers wanted to get manuscripts published for the eager reading public is Martin Luther's *Admonition to Printers*, of September 1525. Erasmus of Rotterdam's indignation at errors due to haste in printing in 1528 is quoted in Kapp, *Deutscher Buchhandel*, pp. 311–12.

[10] Concerning literary societies in Strassburg, Schlettstadt, Tübingen, and elsewhere see Karl Hartfelder, "Erziehung und Unterricht im Zeitalter des Humanismus," in Karl A. Schmid, ed., *Geschichte der Erziehung vom Anfang an bis auf unsere Zeit* (5 vols.; Stuttgart, 1884–1902), II, Part 2, pp. 106–09; for an account of schools, II, Part 2, pp. 114–17.

[11] The Vergil edition of 1502 has the imprint *impressum . . . impensa non mediocri*, "printed . . . at no small cost," by Johannis Grieninger.

[12] On Grüninger's workshop, see Paul Kristeller, *Die Strassburger Bücher-Illustration im XV. und im Anfange des XVI. Jahrhunderts* (Leipzig, 1888), p. 10. As an example of the generally accepted position of Grüninger as Strassburg's outstanding printer of illustrated books, see comments in Richard Muther, *Die Deutsche Bücherillustration der Gothik und Frührenaissance (1460–1530)* (2 vols.; Munich, 1922), I, pp. 75–83, 220–26.

[13] Kristeller, *Die Strassburger Bücher-Illustration*, pp. 7–8. Hase, *Die Koberger*, pp. 130–31, tells of Pirckheimer's hesitation to prepare an edition of Ptolemy for Grüninger, and of the Nürnbergers' plight. In Pirckheimer's own words, "What were we to do since we needed the blocks? . . . He [Grüninger] would not let us have them for a little while at any price."

[14] Grüninger wrote that he had a woodcutter in his house on Sunday, August 13, 1524 (Hase, *Koberger*, "Briefbuch," No. 110). Three documents pertaining to a court action by the guild, *Zur Steltz*, against printer Theodosius Rihel to forbid the employment of a woodcutter during 1571–1572 are reprinted in *Archiv für Geschichte des Deutschen Buchhandels*, V, pp. 96–106.

[15] Werner Cohn, *Einblattdrucke . . . Johannes Grüninger* (Strassburg, 1937),

says that Grüninger did not maintain his own shop after 1510, that his interest in illustrations waned, and that we therefore need not be surprised that no broadside prints have been found later than 1510. I believe that as we shall later see, Grüninger's interest in illustrations continued and overshadowed his craftsmanship as a printer. Kristeller, *Die Strassburger Bücher-Illustration*, p. 8, records a continuous development of Grüninger's establishment from 1495 to 1520. Both authors deal with broadsides and books and do not include maps. With the *Carta Marina* of 1525 the existence of Grüninger's workshop is extended to that year. Muther, *Die Deutsche Bücherillustration*, lists a few new illustrations after that.

[16] Assuming a minimum edition of 500 copies each time, Grüninger printed 2,000 sheets for the *Itineraria* map of Europe in 1511, 1520, and 1527. He printed 25,000 maps, 50 for each copy of the Ptolemy editions of 1522 and 1525. This does not include the 1-page map of Lotharingia. He printed 6,000 sheets for each edition of the *Carta Marina* in 1525, 1527, 1530, and perhaps in 1516; but he probably printed not only 500 but 1,000 maps in 1530, since he published the *Uslegung* and also a Latin guidebook for the map, as we shall later find. This would mean 24,000 sheets for Fries's *Carta Marina* alone. It is almost certain that it was Grüninger who printed the 1,000 Waldseemüller wall maps of 1507, making another 12,000 sheets. This is a total of 98,000 sheets of large folio size and does not include loose-leaf sheets which Grüninger probably printed as advertisements.

[17] A list of publications about Waldseemüller appears in Joseph Fischer and Franz Ritter von Wieser, eds., *Die Älteste Karte mit dem Namen Amerika aus dem Jahre 1507 und die Carta Marina aus dem Jahre 1516* (Innsbruck, 1903), pp. 1–2 (hereafter cited as *Die Älteste Karte*), and Leo Bagrow, ed., *A. Ortelii Catalogus Cartographorum*, in *Petermanns Mitteilungen, Ergänzungsheft*, Nos. 199 and 210 (Gotha, 1928–1930), No. 210, pp. 97–104 (hereafter cited as Bagrow, *Catalogus*). Armand d'Avezac-Macaya, *Martin Hylacomylus Waltzemüller* (hereafter cited as *Waltzemüller*) (Paris, 1867) is very valuable for references even if the author did not know the two large maps and the globe map found later.

[18] Schmidt, *Grüninger*, item No. 85. Gauthier Lud dedicated the book to the Duke René of Lorraine, who died in 1508. For Lud's family background and position in St. Dié, see Avezac-Macaya, *Waltzemüller*, pp. 14–22, and Lucien Gallois, *Les Géographes Allemands de la Renaissance* (Paris, 1890), Chapter IV (Bibliothèque de la Faculté des Lettres de Lyon, Vol. XIII).

[19] For a detailed discussion of the four St. Dié editions and the fifth edition published in Strassburg, see Avezac-Macaya *Waltzemüller*, pp. 36–59, 110–13.

[20] One argument supporting the printing of the first large wall map of 1507 in Grüninger's workshop is in Fischer and Wieser, *Die Älteste Karte*, pp. 16–17.

[21] "Ich habe neue bereitschaft und deckel ein grösere press lüstig zügericht" is the phrase Grüninger uses to show his ability to undertake a big new printing job in 1524. Grüninger to Hans Koberger, February 23, 1524, in Hase, *Koberger*, "Briefbuch," No. 106.

Notes

[22] The public's cordial reception of the map is inferred from a sentence in Waldseemüller's dedicatory letter to Ringmann of February 1508 in *Introductio Architecturae et Perspectivae*, published in *Margarita Philosophica Nova* (Strassburg: Grüninger, 1508) and reprinted in Avezac-Macaya, *Waltzemüller*, pp. 109–10: "Cosmographiam universalem tam solidam quam planam non sine gloria et laude per orbem disseminatam nuper composuimus."

[23] According to Bagrow, *Catalogus*, No. 210, pp. 100–01, the only known copy of the map in its second edition of 1520 has been found at Innsbruck. This means Grüninger certainly saved these blocks until 1520. But on June 24, 1527, he published *Europae seu Chartae itinerariae quo pacto intelligi debeat summaria instructio unacum indice*, a very much reduced new edition containing six and a half pages of alphabetically arranged place names with index numbers. This new index or register, which is very similar to the register in the *Uslegung*, proves that the Waldseemüller map of Europe was published for a third time in 1527. See also August Wolkenhauer, "Sebastian Münsters handschriftliches Kollegienbuch aus den Jahren 1515–1518 und seine Karten," in *Abhandlungen der Königlichen Gesellschaft der Wissenschaften zu Göttingen. Philologisch-historische Klasse*, Neue Folge, Band XI, No. 3 (1909), p. 45, footnote 3.

[24] Avezac-Macaya, *Waltzemüller*, pp. 114–17, proposes Waldseemüller as the author of *Globus Mundi Declaratio* (Strassburg: Grüninger, 1509). Bagrow, *Catalogus*, No. 210, p. 100, thinks it justified to assume Waldseemüller as the author, largely because the same small map representing the earth accompanies the *Cosmographiae Introductio* of 1509 which has the same paper and type as *Globus Mundi Declaratio* and *Der welt-kugel Beschrybung*. The Latin title, *Globus Mundi Declaratio sive Descriptio Mundi*, corresponds to the German, *Der welt-kugel Beschrybung der Welt und des gantzen Ertreichs*. But "darin der Kauffmann und ein ietlicher sehen und mercken mag" is not the equivalent of "qua cuivis etiam mediocriter docto." Poorer still is the German translation of the advertisement: "Wie weit aber also sei von einem ort zu dem andern daz ist mysslich in diser kleinen kuglen zewüssen der grad halb so alhie nit mögen beschriben noch bezeichnet werdenn/sonder so du das begerest zewüssen Mustu unser grosse Mappa anschauwen und speculum orbis/da findestu es eigentlicher ussgetheilt der weite nach/dan gemeinlich. The Latin original is as follows: quantum vero locus unus a reliquo distat, difficile cognitu est in hoc parvo globo propter gradus qui assignari omnes non possunt in eo. Si vero idipsum scire volueris, mappam majorem considerabis cosmographiae planae, in quacertius ac verius apprehendes secundum longum et latum extensos. Waldseemüller's good Latin can be recognized. Grüninger himself could not translate it but no matter who translated it for him, he could check the German, and the suggestion in German to look at "our map" compared with "mappam majorem" is interesting. That the German edition would be ready for the Easter fair and the Latin edition be printed later is very much in keeping with Grüninger's keen interest in publishing in the lay reader's language. Joseph Fischer and Franz Ritter von Wieser,

in their introduction to *The Cosmographiae Introductio of Martin Waldseemüller in Facsimile*, Charles George Herbermann, ed. (New York, 1907), p. 27 (United States Catholic Historical Society, Monograph IV), discuss this same passage with reference to Waldseemüller's authorship rather than to the printer of the map of 1507.

[25] This is one of the rarest anti-Reformation pamphlets because of the attempt by the Strassburg authorities to confiscate the whole edition. It has 53 satirical woodcuts, on some of which Thomas Murner appears with the head of a cat. The image of Luther's foe as a man with a feline head grew very strong among the people and apparently became a tradition. I grew up in a Protestant region of Germany and still remember the use of "Murners" for little cats. For the history of censorship, see Kapp, *Deutscher Buchhandel*, pp. 530–45, and *Archiv für Geschichte des Deutschen Buchhandels*, V, 27. For Strassburg in particular François Ritter, "La Police de l'Imprimerie et de la Librairie à Strasbourg . . .," in *Revue des Bibliothèques*, XXXII (1922), pp. 161–200.

[26] Kapp, *Deutscher Buchhandel*, pp. 402–09, 411, 437. Detailed descriptions of this type of pamphlet literature including *Karsthans* may be found in Karl Hagen, *Deutschlands literarische und religiöse Verhältnisse* (3 vols.; Frankfurt am Main, 1868), II, pp. 177–86.

[27] Kapp, *Deutscher Buchhandel*, p. 417.

[28] See Grüninger's letters to Pirckheimer and Koberger of February 23, June 1 and 14, July 25, August 13, September 1 and 17, and October 18, 1524, in Hase, *Koberger*, "Briefbuch," Nos. 106–13.

[29] The first letter in the series of February 23, 1524, refers to earlier correspondence. In the letter of March 10, 1525, to Koberger, Grüninger says that Pirckheimer would not get the work done even in two years. Hase, *Koberger*, "Briefbuch," No. 120.

[30] Pirckheimer to Grüninger, undated (February 1525) in Hase, *Koberger*, "Briefbuch," No. 118. The contradiction between Pirckheimer's statement that Huttich denied having corrected the Ptolemy of 1525 and Grüninger's reference to Huttich's collaboration cannot be reconciled.

[31] Hase, *Koberger*, "Briefbuch," No. 119.

[32] Grüninger to Koberger, March 10, 1525, in Hase, *Koberger*, "Briefbuch," No. 120.

[33] Grüninger to Pirckheimer, April 6, 1525, in *ibid.*, No. 121.

[34] Grüninger to Koberger, April 24, 1525, in *ibid.*, No. 122. Here he refers to Beatus Rhenanus and other scholarly "fellows" whose standards he would like to observe, although his corrector, a man named Feigensack, could perhaps go ahead according to his own judgment. Beatus Rhenanus was Schlettstadt's outstanding humanist.

[35] For surveys of editions of Ptolemy's *Geographia* in chronological order see: Joseph Sabin, *A Dictionary of Books Relating to America* (29 vols.; New York, 1868–1936), XVI, pp. 43–87; Carlos Sanz, *La Geographia de Ptolomeo* (Madrid,

Notes

1959); Henry N. Stevens, *Ptolemy's Geography*, 2nd ed. (London, 1908); U.S. Library of Congress, *A List of Geographical Atlases in the Library of Congress*, compiled under the direction of Philip Lee Phillips (4 vols.; Washington, 1909–1920), I, pp. 104–30 and *passim*; Justin Winsor, ed., *A Bibliography of Ptolemy's Geography* (Cambridge, Mass., 1884) (Bibliographical Contributions of the Library of Harvard University, No. 18).

[38] Grüninger to Pirckheimer, undated (after April 24, 1525) in Hase, *Koberger*, "Briefbuch," No. 123. The letter clearly indicates that it was written before the publication of the *Uslegung* on September 8, 1525. Additional information on Pirckheimer has been made available with the publication of Emil Reicke's *Willibald Pirckheimers Briefwechsel* (2 vols.; Munich, 1940, 1956). This work, published as volumes 4 and 5 of the Humanistenbriefe series of the Veröffentlichungen der Kommission zur Erforschung der Geschichte der Reformation und Gegenreformation, brings Pirckheimer's correspondence up to the 1515 period, and the contemplated completion of it in two more volumes may throw additional light on his connections with Grüninger. A hint of the possibility of Grüninger's having heard of Pirckheimer's plan to edit another Ptolemy in 1529 is contained in another volume in this series, Erich König, *Konrad Peutingers Briefwechsel* (Munich, 1923), p. 438, which can be connected with Grüninger's letter to Pirckheimer of December 17, 1529, in Hase, *Koberger*, "Briefbuch," No. 129. Grüninger writes that he has "all material preserved together," that is, the wood blocks for the maps, and that the whole edition of the 1525 Ptolemy is sold out.

LORENZ FRIES

[1] The three Greek words written into the edition of 1525 are omitted from the space left for them in 1527; no space is left for them in 1530. They make no sense and are meant to ridicule pseudo-Grecism. I have taken the liberty of rendering *Unkraut*, weed, as rot.

[2] Charles G. A. Schmidt, *Laurent Fries, de Colmar, Médecin, Astrologue, Géographe à Strasbourg et à Metz* (Nancy [1888]). This is the usual thorough work of Strassburg's outstanding historian of literature and very informative, but Schmidt did not know Fries's maps of 1520 and 1525 or the first edition of the *Uslegung*. Bagrow, *Catalogus*, No. 199, pp. 69–74, depicts Fries as "Waldseemüller's apostle." Karl Sudhoff, "Lorenz Fries," *Allgemeine Deutsche Biographie*, XLIV, pp. 770–75, who also mentions Fries in other short writings, adds some details and gives Fries considerable credit as a warmhearted doctor who was progressive for his time (hereafter cited as Sudhoff, *Fries*). None of the biographical information on Fries mentions a broadside of 1513 in the Munich State Library, reproduced in Eugen Holländer, *Wunder, Wundergeburt und Wundergestalt in Einblattdrucken des Fünfzehnten bis Achtzehnten Jahrhunderts* (Stuttgart, 1921), p. 312. Under a stark woodcut of a monster with a head of a cat, born to a woman "not far from Rome" the naive rhymes end with "good wishes to all

from Lorentz Fries." Short references to diseases and to Mars still make it unlikely that Fries as a very young man could have stooped to being a poetaster.

[3] The woodcut portrait is found on the title page of *Artis Memorativae Naturalis et Artifitialis* . . . (Strassburg, 1523), and in its German edition of the same year, both published by Grüninger. Mrs. M. Consuela Oldenbourg, Munich, the authority for woodcut illustrations by Hans Baldung Grien, does not think that Fries's portrait was designed by Grien himself. Mrs. Oldenbourg's letter of March 7, 1962, to me, is gratefully acknowledged. For the best bibliographic references on Grien and his circle see Staatliche Kunsthalle, Karlsruhe, *Hans Baldung Grien* (Karlsruhe, 1959) (hereafter cited as Kunsthalle Karlsruhe, *Grien*).

[4] Schmidt, *Fries*, pp. 1–4 gives several sources for varying information regarding Fries's place of birth. According to *Dictionnaire Encyclopédique des Sciences Médicales*, VI, p. 8, Fries was born in Dokkum and was a Netherlander. *Biographisches Lexikon der hervorragenden Ärtze aller Zeiten und Völker*, II, p. 628 indicates that Fries was born in Strassburg. The confusion about Fries's birthplace originated with a wrong date in "Pantaleon's Prosopographia of 1565," according to Sudhoff in Fielding H. Garrison, ed., *Essays in the History of Medicine* (New York, 1926), p. 289. Charles Abel, *Rabelais, Médecin Stipendié de la Cité de Metz* (Metz, 1870), p. 39, tells of a Pierre le Frison who was appointed city physician at Metz, 1514–1516. *A Dictionary of Books*, XVI, p. 58, calls the editor of Ptolemy in 1522 "Laurentius Fries or Phrisius, a physician and mathematician of Metz." Fries listed Metz but not Colmar among the cities in his *Uslegung*. He published a prognostication in French when he lived in Metz after 1525. Johann Heinrich Zedler, *Grosses Vollständiges Universal-Lexicon*, IX, pp. 2123–24, lists Lorentz Friess or Frisius, a historian of Wuerzburg who, like our Fries, assisted Sebastian Münster with the latter's *Cosmographia*. A Frisius (Laurentius), in Zedler, Vol. 9, p. 2141, of around 1536, is reported as the author of writings which appear to be among those by our Fries, but he is not correctly identified.

[5] Schmidt did not have access to all three editions of the *Uslegung* and used the 1527 edition only. Grieningen is on the *Carta Marina* as Griennig, but in Holland, obviously, as Groeningen.

[6] In *Uslegung*, 1525, Chapter 118, "Von Wien." Also Fries, *Ein Kurtze schirmred der Kunst Astrologie, wider etliche unverstandene vernichter, auch etliche antwurt uff die reden, und fragen, Martini Luthers Augustiners, so er in seinen zehen geboten unformlich wider dise Kunst gethon hat, durch Laurentzen Friesen* (Strassburg: Grüninger, 1520), p. 2.

[7] Fries mentions medical schools in Piacenza, Padua, and Montpellier "where the noble art of medicine is flourishing and the shoelaces of whose masters of medicine I would not dare to untie" in the second chapter of the first book in the *Spiegel der Artzney*. Sudhoff's inquiry at Montpellier about Fries's doctorate remained unanswered, according to Garrison, *Essays in the History of Medicine*, p. 289.

Notes

[8] The name syphilis for gallic disease originated with Hieronymus Fracastorius' medical poem of 1530, *Syphilis, sive Morbus Gallicus*, published in Verona.

[9] The Latin tract *De Morbo Gallico Opusculum* was reprinted in Basel in 1532 under the title *Epitome Opusculi de Curandis Pustulis Ulceribus et Doloribus Morbi Gallici.*

[10] *Ein gründtlich und bestendig heilung aller schäden, beulen, löcher (oder was des gleichen) am leib des menschen, mit gar geringen kosten, mit dem tranck des holtzes guaiaco* (Strassburg: J. Pruss, 1539) must have appeared for the first time before September 1, 1518, because Fries says at the end of the *Spiegel*: "About the skin disease of the French you find my separate publications in Latin and German."

[11] Schmidt, *Fries*, p. 6.

[12] *Spiegel der Artzney*, third part of the first book, Chapter XIII, tells of the usefulness of the pharmacy.

[13] Hieronymus Brunschwig, *Dis ist das buch der Cirurgia* (Strassburg: Grüninger, 1497), and *Liber de Arte Distillandi de Simplicibus. Das Buch der rechten Kunst zu distillieren* . . . (Strassburg: Grüninger, 1500). Both books went through several editions.

[14] Johann von Gersdorff, *Feldtbuch der Wundtartzney* (Strassburg, 1517).

[15] This is one of the most frequently reproduced woodcuts and is used as one of six contemporary illustrations of the work of doctors under "learned professions" in Eugen Diederichs, *Deutsches Leben der Vergangenheit in Bildern* (Jena, 1908), pp. 82–83. Detailed listings of its re-uses and a reproduction in the catalog are published by Kunsthalle Karlsruhe, *Grien*, pp. 359–61. The medical illustrations, which Grüninger reduced in size for the edition of the *Spiegel* in 1519, are discussed in Muther, *Deutsche Bücherillustration*, p. 211.

[16] For editions, see Sudhoff, *Fries*, p. 772; Schmidt, *Fries*, pp. 27–29. Schmidt, p. 22, lists another partial reprint of 1559. The copy of the edition of 1529, published by Balthasar Beck in Strassburg, in the municipal library of Strassburg has a rhymed handwritten note under the title: "The book I have bought. Caspar I was baptized, Washer I am called. Alsace is my country," with the date November 10, 1607. See François Ritter, *Catalogue des Incunables et Livres du XVIe Siècle de la Bibliothèque Municipale de Strasbourg* (Strasbourg, 1948), p. 339, No. 1025.

[17] Sudhoff, *Abhandlungen von Sudhoff*, pp. 117–20. Compare Schmidt, *Fries*, pp. 15–16.

[18] *Spiegel*, editions of 1530 and 1532, preface by Fries, dated July 23, 1530. Fries uses the term *Heumond*, month of hay, which is July.

[19] Schmidt, *Fries*, p. 17. Quoted from *Spiegel*, 1532 edition, fol. 136 verso. The ancient traditions of Galen and Ptolemy about the determining of the critical days in illness by iatromathematicians are discussed by Karl Sudhoff, "Zur Geschichte der Lehre von den kritischen Tagen im Krankheitsverlaufe," in *Wiener Medizinische Wochenschrift*, LII (1902), No. 5, pp. 209–13; No. 6, pp. 272–75;

No. 7, pp. 321–25; No. 8, pp. 371–74 (my source: *Abhandlungen von Sudhoff*, pp. 1–22).

[20] Claudius Ptolemy, *Geographia* (Strassburg, 1522), p. 7, has a remark about Colmar's barbaric citizens who persecute all literature. Schmidt, *Fries*, p. 8, uses this as an explanation for Fries's leaving the city. The fact that Fries returned to Colmar docs not suggest a lasting dislike.

[21] Schmidt, *Fries*, pp. 24–30. In spite of its poor quality the tract was reprinted in 1535 and 1579.

[22] Sudhoff, *Fries*, p. 772. Grüninger took the following new books to the Frankfurt fair in 1519: Fries's tract on *Der Wildbeder Natur* and the second edition of the *Spiegel*; Ulrich von Hutten's book on guayac, translated into German by Thomas Murner; and another edition of Brunschwig's *Kunst zu distillieren* all published between July 24 and September 1, 1519.

[23] Fries distinguishes between artificial and natural baths in Chapter VI, part 3 of Book I, in the *Spiegel*. A detailed discussion of the book of *Der Wildbeder Natur* is in Schmidt, *Fries*, pp. 34–35.

[24] The woodcut is discussed in Muther, *Deutsche Bücherillustration*, p. 217. For a discussion of pictorial representations showing people eating and drinking in the public baths see Fielding H. Garrison, *An Introduction to the History of Medicine* (Philadelphia, 1914), p. 173.

[25] This interpretation is based on Fries's preface of 1530 which was published in the *Spiegel*, 1532.

[26] Sudhoff, *Fries*, p. 771. Fries's salary of 143 livres for eight months' service is recorded in the municipal accounts of 1519.

[27] Entry of October 23, 1520, in Wittmer and Meyer, *Livre de Bourgeoisie*, 11, p. 662. The same connection between printers and doctors is described in Florence by Erwin H. Ackerknecht, *A Short History of Medicine* (New York, 1955), p. 88.

[28] The only reference to Fries's family is the letter which Paracelsus wrote from Colmar to Amerbach in Basel on February 28, 1528, where he says that he was excellently received by Fries and his family. See *Theophrast von Hohenheim, gennant Paracelsus, Sämtliche Werke*. I. Abteilung. *Die medizinischen, naturwissenschaftlichen und naturphilosophischen Schriften*, Karl Sudhoff, ed. (14 vols.; Munich, 1922–1933), VI, pp. 34–35, Table IV.

[29] *Spiegel*, 1523, "Von der Ländern."

[30] Schmidt, *Fries*, p. 43.

[31] Strassburg, 1520. Luther's condemnation of astrology appeared in his explanation of the first commandment in *Decem Praecepta Wittenbergensi Praedicata Populo* (Leipzig, 1518), fol. A4.

[32] Schmidt, *Fries*, pp. 39–41, 47. The play has been dated on the basis of the reference to Fries by Karl Lendi, "Der Dichter Pamphilus Gengenbach," *Sprache und Dichtung*, Heft 39 (1926), p. 39.

[33] C. Julius Solinus, *Polyhistor*, Johannes Camers, ed. (Vienna, 1520). The map

Notes

and the preface by Camers both bear the date 1520, although they were presumably prepared independently.

[34] We do not know exactly how the peculiar copies of the Waldseemüller maps, which Joseph Fischer discovered in 1901, got into the library of Johann Schöner in Nürnberg. The fact that two sheets of the wall map of 1507 have a square grid, usually used for purposes of reduction, points to the possibility that these sheets were used by Fries for his reduction; see pp. 41, 57.

[35] Compare Bagrow, *Catalogus*, No. 199, pp. 31–33, 70; Fischer and Wieser, *Die Älteste Karte*, p. 40; Hermann Wagner, "Die dritte Weltkarte Peter Apians v. J. 1530 und die Pseudo-Apianische Weltkarte von 1551," *Nachrichten von der Königlichen Gesellschaft der Wissenschaften zu Göttingen*, 1892, pp. 541–72; see 545–49 in particular. Wagner does not mention Fries at all. Siegmund Gunther, "Peter und Philipp Apian, zwei deutsche Mathematiker und Kartographen," *Abhandlungen der Königlichen Böhmischen Gesellschaft der Wissenschaften*, Series 6, Vol. XI (1882), Mathematische naturwissenschaftliche Classe, No. 4, pp. 67–68.

[36] The two Latin inscriptions read: "Hec terra cum adiacentib[us] insulis inuenta est per Columbu[m] ianuensem ex mandato Regis Castelle" (Ptolemy, 1513) and "Anno 1497 hec terra cum adiace[n]tib[us] insula inventa est per Columbum Ianuensem ex mandato regis Castello" (Apian's world map, 1520). The guayac inscription on a globe map of 1518 is reported by Sophus Ruge, "Die Entwicklung der Kartographie von Amerika bis 1570," No. 106, *Ergänzungsheft Petermanns Mitteilungen*, p. 42.

[37] Bagrow, *Catalogus*, I, p. 70. Peter Apian was born in 1495 and was at the university of Leipzig in 1516; he probably came to Vienna after Fries had been there. Fries might have known Camers from his days in Vienna where the latter taught mathematics and geography; a connecting link might have been George Tannstetter under whom Apian, Sebastian Münster, and other cosmographers studied.

[38] The only lead to a date more specific than 1520 may be found in the following inscription under the title: "Caroli V Imperii, Anno I." Charles V was elected emperor on June 28, 1519, and crowned October 23, 1519, which would put the date of Schott's publications before June 28, 1520.

[39] The rhinoceros, knowledge of which had reached Nürnberg in 1513 through the letter of a German printer from Lisbon, appears to have stirred the European imagination; even Albrecht Dürer made an engraving in its honor. See Ernest George Ravenstein, *Martin Behaim, His Life and His Globe* (London, 1908), p. 2, footnote 4.

[40] A biographical sketch of Thomas Vogler, a teacher at the cathedral school, is in Charles G. A. Schmidt, *Histoire Littéraire de l'Alsace à la Fin du XVe et au Commencement du XVIe Siècle* (2 vols.; Paris, 1879), II, pp. 149–54.

[41] I have based this presentation on the following sources: Grüninger's letter to Koberger, February 23, 1524, in Hase, *Koberger*, "Briefbuch," No. 106; Fries's

preface to the *Uslegung*, 1525; data about Grüninger's publications in Schmidt, *Grüninger*, for the years 1520 to 1522; Thomas Vogler's preface to *Ptolemy*, 1522; Fries's note in the *Ptolemy*, p. 100. Bagrow, *Catalogus*, No. 210, "Martin Waldseemüller," p. 101, arrived at the conclusion that Fries prepared the maps in reduced size and that part of the *blocks* were ready in 1518. All bibliographies of Ptolemy agree that the 1520 edition was printed from the same blocks as that of 1513. The reduced size does not appear before 1522. Bagrow's statement, *Catalogus*, No. 199, p. 72, that the year 1518 "under the picture of Emperor Maximilian," on the map of "Tabula Moderna Germaniae," proves that one of the map blocks was already cut in 1518, can be disputed. This picture and the legend below it are doubtless one piece fitted into the block of the map. This does not prove that the map was made in 1518. The picture probably came from the collection of material for the *Chronica Mundi* in Grüninger's shop.

[42] Bagrow, *Catalogus*, No. 199, pp. 71–77, lists 51 maps for the 1522 edition. The order of the maps is apparently different in the copy used by Bagrow from that in the Bell Collection. Winsor, *Bibliography of Ptolemy's Geography*, p. 13, lists 49 maps, and Georg Wolfgang Panzer, *Annales Typographici* (11 vols.; Nürnberg, 1793–1803), VI, p. 98, 47. Schmidt, *Grüninger*, p. 80, gives 51. Sabin, *Dictionary of Books*, XVI, p. 58, writes that "the 50 woodcut maps are each on two leaves, with one exception."

[43] There is also a difference in the cities of the Upper Rhine region. In 1513, Speyer, Landau, Hagenau, Strassburg, Schlettstadt, Colmar, ense (Ensisheim), oden (St. Odilien), Mühlhausen, and Basel are shown; in 1522, Worms, Speyer, Hagenau, Strassburg, Schlettstadt, Colmar, Basel, and Freiburg.

[44] The association between the passage about infertile Palestine from the 1522 Ptolemy which reappeared in the 1535 and 1541 editions and its role in the condemnation and burning of Michael Servetus appears to have started with a "curious history." See Johann L. Mosheim, *An Ecclesiastical History*, Archibald Maclaine, ed. and trans. (4 vols.; New York, 1821), III, pp. 356–57, note. Panzer, *Annales Typographici*, VI, p. 98, and Henry Harrisse, *Bibliotheca Americana Vetustissima* (New York, 1866), p. 202, add to their notes on the Ptolemy of 1522, "Extat in hac editione perrara ad tertiam Africae [which is wrong] mappam iam famosus iste de Palaestina locus, qui Serveto postea tanquam atrox crimen imputabatur, Cf. Mosheimii Ander Vers. einer Ketzergeschichte, p. 260 sqq." There is no need to list subsequent repetitions, a recent one being Carlos Sanz, *La Geographia de Ptolomeo* (Madrid, 1959), p. 173, where the title page of Tabula Terre Sanctae is reproduced with this description: Página con la descripción de Tierra Santa o Palestina, en la que aparece el famoso pasaje, por el que fué inculpado en el proceso, en el cual se le condenó a morir en la hoguera, y del que no fué autor. The thorough investigation by John C. Hemmeter, "Michael Servetus, Discoverer of the Pulmonary Circulation, His Life and Work," *Janus*, XX (1915), pp. 331–64, points out "that the scientific and physiological teachings were not introduced as an element of antagonism." Joseph Sabin, in *Dictionary*

of Books, XVI, puts it this way: "The account of Palestine wrongly attributed to Servetus, served as one of the pretexts for his execution," p. 59; "The descriptive text was omitted from several of the maps [of the 1541 edition] including that relating to Palestine," p. 63; "Many copies of this book [the 1535 edition] are said to have been burned at the same time [as the trial and execution of Servetus] by the orders of Calvin," p. 61. This gave rise to the commercial approach in Otto Harrassowitz, *Tausend alte Drucke aus drei Jahrhunderten, Bücher-Katalog 392* (Leipzig, 1922), p. 19, where a Ptolemy of 1535 is listed with this comment, which I translate: "First printing of this famous edition by Michael Servetus, which is remarkable for this reason. Through an unpremeditated reprint of a derogatory remark about the Holy Land from the Ptolemy edition of 1522, Calvin and his adherents got a pretext which led to the banning and execution of unhappy Servetus. For the incriminating passage of the Holy Land alone, which was suppressed in the second edition of 1541, Calvin ordered the burning of all copies that he could put his hands on with fanatical zeal, which explains its particular rarity." Historians of geography will do well to forget the myth or investigate it with the help of documents about the trial before nursing it any further.

[45] The monogram "G" at the lower end of the pillar to the left of the front page of Tabula V Europae suggests no particular artist. Schmidt, *Grüninger*, p. 80, states that "I H," found eight times in the same design of the centerpiece on front pages, may be by Jean (Hans) Herbst or Herbster, but Hans Koegler, in Ulrich Thieme and Felix Becker, *Allgemeines Lexikon der Bildenden Künstler* (37 vols.; Leipzig, 1907–1950), XVI, p. 451 (hereafter cited as Thieme-Becker, *Künstler-Lexikon*), rejects this suggestion. Ritter, *Histoire de l'Imprimerie Alsacienne*, p. 98, mentions Jerome Hopferd of Augsburg as a possibility. I suggest that "N K," appearing twice in a centerpiece, is Nikolas Kremer, on the basis of the data given in Kunsthalle Karlsruhe, *Grien*, pp. 122–23, Thieme-Becker, *Künstler-Lexikon*, XXI, p. 494, and Paul Wescher, "Nikolas Kremer of Strassburg," in *Art Quarterly*, I (1938), p. 204–11. I have found no identification of "H S" and "M A" which appear often in a banderole.

[46] Lorenz Fries, *Artis Memorativae Naturalis et Artifitialis* . . . (Strassburg: Grüninger, 1523), *Kurtzer bericht wie man die gedechtniss wunderbarlichen stercken mag*. Sudhoff, *Fries*, p. 773, dates this German edition 1523.

[47] According to Sudhoff, *Fries*, pp. 773–74, Fries wrote two prognostications in 1523 for 1524. One, without date or place, *Trostliche bewerung das der jüngst tag noch in vil jahren nitt kume. Auch das sein zeit niemanss wysse dann got*, is addressed to Luther's article about the "Christian and well-founded proof of the Day of Judgment." Schmidt, *Fries*, p. 43, discusses the other, a copy of which is in the university library of Göttingen, *Ein zusamen gelesen urteyl ausz den alten erfarnen meistern der astrologÿ über die grossen zusamenkunfft Saturni und Jovis in dem M.D.XXIIII. jar.*

[48] Ritter, *Histoire de l'Imprimerie*, p. 412: "*Der Juden Practica*, pronostics pour l'année 1525." Farckall worked as a printer in Colmar from 1522 to the be-

ginning of 1524. He then went to Frankfurt and from there to Hagenau, where he probably stayed until 1529. In 1530 he was in Strassburg and Grüninger printed three books at his expense that year. *Ibid.*, pp. 102, 376, 411–14, 470. The puzzling aspect is that Farckall was a printer and publisher of Reformation literature.

[49] Grüninger to Pirckheimer, June 1, 1524, "Ich mach eine newe Carthamarina," in Hase, *Koberger*, "Briefbuch," No. 107.

[50] Grüninger to Koberger, August 13, 1524, "I have a formcutter in the house who is cutting more things for the *Carta Marina* . . . I have written you before about the *Chronica Mundi* and the *Carta Marina* and sent you figures." In a postscript he said, "And also Dr. Fries plans something which had not been there before," Hase, *Koberger*, "Briefbuch," No. 110; Grüninger to Koberger, September 1, 1524, "Please don't forget about the *Carta Marina*," *ibid.*, No. 111; Grüninger to Koberger, September 17, 1524, "Thank you for the bona speranca," *ibid.*, No. 112; Grüninger to Koberger, February 26, 1525, "I will send Mr. Pirckheimer a pretty new map as a gift which should be worth five gülden. I have had it cut anew and smaller and quite pretty," *ibid.*, No. 116. The preface by Fries is dated "When the sun was in the twenty-first degree and forty minutes in the sign of the fish, 1525." The sign of the fish means from February 21 to March 21; figured at 30 degrees per month, the day would be March 12.

[51] Wittmer and Meyer, *Le Livre de Bourgeoisie*, II, p. 709 for Vogler; p. 713 for Gebwiler; p. 739 for Fries. How little the recording of citizenship means in the case of Gebwiler is also stressed by Karl Stenzel, "Die Strassburger Chronik des elsässischen Humanisten Hieronymus Gebwiler," in *Schriften des Wissenschaftlichen Instituts der Elsass-Lothringer im Reich an der Universität Frankfurt a.M.*, No. 10 (1926), p. 15. For Gebwiler's anti-Reformation attitude, see Charles G. A. Schmidt, *Histoire Littéraire de l'Alsace à la Fin du XV*[e] *et au Commencement du XVI*[e] *Siècle* (2 vols.; Paris, 1879), II, pp. 166–67. Vogler, the aforementioned friend of Fries who wrote the introduction for the Ptolemy of 1522, is not mentioned after 1525 as being at the Strassburg cathedral; he retired to the convent at Stephansfeld. See Schmidt, *Histoire*, p. 154.

[52] Abel, *Rabelais*, pp. 41–44; Sudhoff, *Fries*, p. 771.

[53] The investigation of the controversy between Fries and Paracelsus is the contribution of Karl Sudhoff.

THE MAP AND THE BOOK

[1] *Uslegung*, preface, all three editions.

[2] I am indebted to John Parker for measuring the map in Munich in the summer of 1961 and to Robert Bauman of the Audio-Visual Department at Macalester College for assistance in mounting the photostat copy. The best and most complete collation of the map is in Walther Ruge, "Aelteres kartographisches Material in deutschen Bibliotheken. Vierter Bericht über die Jahre 1906–1909."

Notes

Nachrichten von der Königlichen Gesellschaft der Wissenschaften zu Göttingen. Philologisch-historische Klasse, 1911, pp. 62–63. The first announcement of the finding of the *Carta Marina* was in Karl Sudhoff, "Lorenz Friesen's Weltkarte in Zwölf Blättern aus dem Jahre 1525," *Beilage zur Norddeutschen Allgemeinen Zeitung*, No. 56, March 7, 1902.

[3] *Uslegung*, all three editions, last paragraph.

[4] Fischer and Wieser, *Die Älteste Karte*, p. 3, say that "the size of each sheet including the white margin is 45.5 by 62 cm." Bagrow, *Catalogus*, No. 210, p. 103, gives 445 by 620 millimeters. W. Ruge, *Nachrichten·von der . . . Gesellschaft . . . zu Göttingen*, 1911, p. 62, gives for the total size of Fries's map "1876 (1867) x 1013 (1031) millimeters," and Bagrow, *Catalogus*, No. 199, p. 72, describes it as 1,155 by 2,000 millimeters. The comparative measurements quoted in the text are based on measuring the sheets in the facsimile atlas, not including white margins, and on measurements of the *Carta Marina* in Munich. It should be emphasized that different measurements can result from including or excluding lines or letters that may be considered part of the map or not, particularly on the two center sheets. The discussion here is restricted to those figures which help to shed light on the problem of the reduction. The average of 10 per cent reduction in width is based on all twelve sheets, the reduction of which varies from 4.2 to 13.9 per cent, compared with the corresponding sheets in the *Carta Marina* of 1516.

[5] Fischer and Wieser, *Die Älteste Karte*, pp. 5–6. The authors do not elaborate on the purpose of the grid which, incidentally, is also found on two of the twelve sheets of the wall map of 1507, discovered together with the *Carta Marina* of 1516 and reproduced in the same atlas.

[6] For biographical data on Johannes Schöner see *Allgemeine Deutsche Biographie*, XXXII, pp. 295–97, largely based on Zedler, *Universal-Lexikon*, XXXV, p. 991; Henry N. Stevens, *Johann Schöner* (London, 1888); Franz R. von Wieser, "Der verschollene Globus des Johannes Schöner von 1523," *Sitzungsberichte der Philosophisch-Historischen Classe der kaiserlichen Akademie der Wissenschaften*, CXVII (1889), Abhandlung 5, pp. 1–18. Joseph Fischer, *Die Entdeckungen der Normannen in Amerika* (Freiburg im Breisgau, 1902), pp. 94–96, discusses Schöner's use of Waldseemüller's maps.

[7] Reicke, *Pirckheimers Briefwechsel*, I, p. VII and p. XIX, footnote. Pirckheimer wrote about the plan to publish new maps with equidistant meridians in his dedication to Bishop Sebastian Sperantium of Brisen in the Ptolemy in 1525. Franz R. von Wieser, "A. E. v. Nordenskiölds Facsimile-Atlas," *Petermanns Mitteilungen* XXXVI (1890), pp. 270–80, reprints this passage in a footnote on p. 274 and rejects Nordenskiöld's idea that Pirckheimer anticipated the Mercator projection. For our context it is important to note that Pirckheimer wrote "Ego quidem, si Deus permiserit novas aliquando tabulas edere constitui, meridianis aequidistantibus, ut Ptolemaeus jubet." Written before his disappointment over the Ptolemy publication, this passage fits the situation very well.

[8] Fischer and Wieser, *Die Älteste Karte*, p. 39, footnote 3: "Martinus Wald-seemüller, Universalem nauigatoriam (quam Marinam vulgo appelant) in Ger-mania editam." The full title of the *Carta Marina* by Waldseemüller is *Carta marina navigatoria Portugallen. navigationes atque tocius cogniti orbis terre marisque formam naturamque situs et terminos nostris temporibus recognitos et ab antiquorum traditione differentes, eciam quor[um] vetusti non meminerunt autores hec generaliter indicate.* Fischer and Wieser, *Die Älteste Karte*, p. 19.

[9] Wolkenhauer, *Abhandlungen der . . . Gesellschaft . . . zu Göttingen*, XI, No. 3. The dates for the notebook are listed systematically after careful investiga-tion on pp. 31–32. According to pp. 45–46, some of the maps may have been copied before 1513. But this does not rule out the possibility that Münster could have added copies until 1518 if he had wanted to.

[10] Fischer and Wieser, *Die Älteste Karte*, p. 40, refer to topographic legends in India, numerous details in decorative drawings, and the representation of the hydrography and topography of South Africa. Heinrich Averdunk and Dr. J. Müller-Reinhard, "Gerhard Mercator und die Geographen unter seinen Nach-kommen," *Ergänzungsheft zu Petermanns Mitteilungen*, No. 182 (1914), p. 30, mention one detail of the 1569 world map of Mercator — the animal with the pouch and its young, which "is not missing" when the map is compared with the *Carta Marina* of 1516. But Fries's map also has that detail. These authors explain the famous projection of Mercator's world map of 1569 without referring to the *Carta Marina* of 1516 (pp. 65–72).

[11] The reference to new marine charts in Johannes Schöner's *Opusculum Ge-ographicum* (Nürnberg, 1533) is not specific. The passage at the end of Chapter 6 reads: "quae etiam uidere licebit in praesenti opere sphaerico ipsius terrae, ac in nouissimis cartis marinarijs, quarum nos plures etiam notabiles magnae aestima-tionis ad manus habuimus in hac nostra descriptione." This could refer equally well to the Waldseemüller set with hand-drawn grid or to the *Carta Marina* of 1525–1530.

[12] The most recent publication about the *Carta Marina* of 1525 is Leo Bagrow, "Fragments of the 'Carta Marina' by Laurentius Fries, 1524," *Imago Mundi*, XIV (1950), p. 111. The article was published posthumously and contains several minor errors, one of them the date in the title. These are fragments of the West Africa sheet. I have been unable to draw any significant conclusions about Fries's copying on the basis of the peculiarities of West Africa sheet bb; it is the one loose leaf in the bound set of Waldseemüller's maps, and its tracing with the grid added is bound. The loose sheet has a different watermark from all the others in the set of 1516; it is the only sheet without a watermark in 1525. A piece of this sheet, used for binding another book, is reported to be the same as the West African sheet of the Fries edition prior to the filling of the frames with printed legends. The only conclusion that one can draw is that a number of these West Africa sheets seem to have been available.

[13] Fischer and Wieser, *Die Älteste Karte*, pp. 31–34, discuss the influence of

Notes

the Canerio map on Waldseemüller in detail and list the other sources for the *Carta Marina* which Waldseemüller named himself on the large shield at the lower left.

[14] A very informative investigation of "The History of Geographical Map Projections until 1600" by Johannes Keuning, *Imago Mundi*, XII (1955), pp. 1–24, discusses the modified Marinus projection on pp. 13–14. He does not mention the *Carta Marina*, but on p. 15 he groups the Orbis Typus map in the 1513 Ptolemy, the forerunner of Waldseemüller's *Carta Marina*, with quadratic plane maps where "the degrees on the meridian and those on the equator are of the same length." This is different from Mercator's projection with increasing latitudes, for which Erhard Etzlaub of Nürnberg provides more of a precedent — with a little map of between 1511 and 1513 — than does Waldseemüller's *Carta Marina*, *Imago Mundi*, XII (1955), p. 17.

[15] *Uslegung*, 1525, p. 4.

[16] For an investigation of the availability of knowledge about the Straits of Magellan between 1515 and 1520, see Franz R. von Wieser, *Magalhâes-Strasse und Austral-Continent auf den Globen des Johannes Schöner* (Innsbruck, 1881).

[17] Wolkenhauer, *Abhandlungen der . . . Gesellschaft . . . zu Göttingen*, XI, No. 3, p. 43, writes that "Münsters Kopien sind infolge der Verkleinerung bedeutend inhaltsärmer." Averdunk and Müller-Reinhard, "Gerhard Mercator . . .," *Ergänzungsheft zu Petermanns Mitteilungen*, No. 182, p. 73, state with reference to Ortelius's world map of 1570 reduced from Mercator's world map of 1569: "Because of the smaller scale many places, rivers, lakes, and mountains and their names are missing."

[18] This became clear to me through studies of French fur-trading routes and of the watershed concept in American political geography of the colonial period. For a specific example, see my "Science and Historical Truth on French Maps of the 17th and 18th Centuries," *Proceedings of the Minnesota Academy of Science*, XXV–XXVI (1957–1958), pp. 327–37. The validity of this point of view was strengthened after I listened to a number of papers at the 19th International Geographic Congress in Stockholm in 1960, and after conversation with Eduard Imhof of the University of Zürich, Chairman of the Section on Geographical and Cartography and Photogeography at the Congress, who agreed, and who is immeasurably better qualified than I to make methodological statements about the history of cartography.

[19] An early warning came from Johann George Kohl (1808–1887). The passage, undated, but apparently from 1852, quoted in connection with Kohl's studies of the Ptolemy of 1513, Schöner's globe map, and a mysterious world map of 1527, deserves full translation: "We should warn of too eager a usage of these old materials. Admittedly, these maps pretend to show the picture of a land in its main features in such a way as they were believed to be at the time of their production. But merely the business of drawing the maps, which should have been the work only of very knowledgeable and scholarly men, was often in badly un-

educated hands and performed in extremely negligent fashion." H. A. Schumacher, "Kohl's Amerikanische Studien," *Deutsche Geographische Blätter*, XI (1880), p. 122. This warning was repeated by another great scholar of early historical cartography of America, Sophus Ruge, "Die Entwicklung der Kartographie von Amerika bis 1570," *Ergänzungsheft zu Petermanns Mitteilunger*, No. 106 (1892), p. 9.

[20] Fischer and Wieser, *Die Älteste Karte*, p. 22. The comparison of names along the West African coast was helped by the use of comparative tables of place names on seven maps — from the Hamy map to Waldseemüller's *Carta Marina* — given in Fischer and Wieser, pp. 45–52.

[21] Fries omitted .P. Dearena at the mouth of the river with Cannibales; he also omitted the group of five names — Bareras Vermeias, Rio de Brazil, Barossa, Mont Pasqual, Rio de S Lucia along the coast — and, after Serra de .S. Thome, the following five at intervals: Alape de S Paulo, Baic Derees, Pinachullo Detentio, Rio de S Anthonio, Porto de Vincecio, Fischer and Wieser, *Die Älteste Karte*, pp. 54–55.

[22] The German text in the *Uslegung* says "Ein merkart der portugalesichen vnd gantzen erkanten welt sthiffungen des ertreichs vnd mers/gestalt/natur gelegenheiten vnd gegnen/nüwlichen widerumb gebesseret/vnd von dargebung der alten vnder schiden/ingemein/anzögend" (1525 ed., fol. Aii).

[23] Fischer and Wieser, *Die Älteste Karte*, p. 22, think there is some doubt.

[24] Dr. Alois Fauser, state library of Munich, was so kind as to examine the numbers closely with me. He agreed that they could have been set in. I am convinced that they are. The date itself must be read 1530, although it looks like 1730 because of the way the number 5 began to be printed during this period.

[25] An example is found in the letter to Koberger from Thoman Anshelm of Basel, January 7, 1518, who was then trying to get paper from mills around Strassburg. Hase, *Koberger*, "Briefbuch" No. 105.

[26] The oxhead is a frequently occurring watermark and is reproduced in Paul Heitz, *Les Filigranes des Papiers Contenus dans les Archives de la Ville de Strassbourg* (Strassburg, 1902), Plate V, No. 54. An anchor in a circle with very slight variation is also the watermark on the loose-leaf West Africa sheet of 1516, whereas all the other sheets of both earlier maps, the 1507 wall map, and the *Carta Marina* of 1516 have the same watermark — a crown.

[27] *Uslegung*, all three editions, Chapter 7, first part.

[28] Cutters of designs and of letters appear to have been separate craftsmen at that time. A Peter Kreus, who became a citizen in 1520, is a *geschryft schnyder*, while woodcutters were *formenschneider*. Compare Hans Rott, *Quellen und Forschungen zur süd-westdeutschen und Schweizerischen Kunstgeschichte im XV. und XVI. Jahrhundert* III, Der Oberrhein, Quellen I (Baden, Pfalz, Elsass) (1926), p. 276.

[29] Fries has: Terra de cuba partis affrice, Waldseemüller: Terra de Cuba Asie Partis.

Notes

[30] Kapp, *Deutscher Buchhandel*, pp. 322–25, lists a number of specific examples of the size of editions. We know from the note by Waldseemüller on his *Carta Marina* of 1516 that Grüninger printed 1,000 copies of the Ptolemy map. Grüninger restricted the edition of the Ptolemy to 500 in 1525, but hoped also to print a German Ptolemy of 500. See his letter of February 23, 1524, to Koberger in Hase, *Koberger*, "Briefbuch," No. 106.

[31] Grüninger was probably no longer able, for financial reasons, to engage Grien by 1524 or 1525. There is a noticeable kinship between the sea lion of 1525 and the drawings of a seal and cow, which may be by Grien, in Carl Koch, *Die Zeichnungen Hans Baldung Griens* (Berlin, 1941), reproductions 201 and 202, and text on p. 45.

[32] George Glockendon printed a road map in Nürnberg in 1501; Albrecht Glockendon, his son, was an "illuminist" in 1533, according to August Wolkenhauer, "Der Nürnberger Kartograph Erhard Etzlaub," *Deutsche Geographische Blätter*, XXX (1907), p. 67. See also Wolkenhauer's "Über die ältesten Reisekarten von Deutschland aus dem Ende des 15. und dem Anfange des 16. Jahrhunderts," *Deutsche Geographische Blätter*, XXVI (1903), p. 131. For information on George Glockendon as illuminator of the Behaim globe, see Ravenstein, *Martin Behaim*, p. 59; regarding payment received for painting the sphere for 15 weeks, p. 112. None of the Glockendons listed by Th. Hampe in Thieme-Becker, *Künstler-Lexikon*, XIV, pp. 257–361, appears to have had connections with Strassburg. The detail of twelve sons is mentioned by Hase, *Koberger*, p. 114, who quotes George W. K. Lochner, ed., *Des Johann Neudörfer . . . Nachrichten von Künstlern und Werkleuten daselbst aus dem Jahre 1547 . . .*, No. 10 (Vienna, 1875). The globe is beautifully reproduced on four separate folded maps in Ravenstein, *Martin Behaim*.

[33] The facsimile of 1926 on which I discovered the monogram has "Fo." John Parker, who checked the monogram on the original in 1961, found that the "o" was a penciled addition, which thereupon was erased by the curator of the map collection at the state library of Munich.

[34] For an explanation of Waldseemüller's use of the symbol of the crescent, which is located in the same position – i.e., in the north of South America – on the Canerio maps, see Fischer and Wieser, *Die Älteste Karte*, p. 30, footnote 2. Good examples of perfect wind rose arrangements are found on the Portuguese chart of the Indian Ocean of 1509, reproduced in Richard Uhden, "The Oldest Portuguese Original Chart of the Indian Ocean, A.D., 1509," *Imago Mundi*, III (1939), pp. 7–11, and on the sea chart designed by Oronce Finé in 1532, reproduced in Lloyd A. Brown, *The Story of Maps* (Boston, 1950), p. 135.

[35] *Uslegung*, all editions, Chapter 5.

[36] This use of mountains as symbols has been observed on many maps; the technique of indicating divides by sharply drawn mountain crests was used as late as the eighteenth century. See my "French Canada and the Ohio Country," *The Canadian Geographer*, No. 12 (1958), p. 2; "Zur historischen und rechtlichen

Problematik von Grenze und Flussgebiet in Nordamerika," *Forschungen zu Staat und Verfassung*, Festgabe für Fritz Hartung, ed. by Richard Dietrich and Gerhard Oestreich (Berlin, 1958), pp. 310–13; also *Proceedings of the Minnesota Academy of Science*, XXV–XXVI, pp. 327–37.

[37] Edward Lynam, "The Character of England in Maps," *The Geographical Magazine*, XVIII (1945), pp. 2–9, 56–64, has good examples of the pictorial symbols used for towns along the roads.

[38] For a thorough discussion of Roman *itineraria*, including the so-called Peutinger tables, see August Friedrich von Pauly, *Pauly's Real-Encyclopädie der Classischen Altertumswissenschaft*, neue Bearb. begonnen von Georg Wissowa (Stuttgart, 1894–), IX, pp. 2307–63, "Itinerarien." Oscar A. Seyffert, *A Dictionary of Classical Antiquities*, rev. and ed. by Henry Nettleship and J. E. Sandys (London, 1891), p. 328, "Itineraria," is too abbreviated on this topic. Etzlaub's road maps, published with the title "Das sein dy lantstrassen durch das Romisch reych von einem Kunigreych zw dem andern dy an Tewtsche land stossen von meilen zw meilen mit puncten verzeichnet" (Nürnberg, 1501), are discussed in Wolkenhauer, *Deutsche Geographische Blätter*, XXX (1907), p. 67.

[39] Another citation of a woodcut map with roads in the environment of Nürnberg is given in W. Ruge, *Nachrichten von der . . . Gesellschaft . . . zu Göttingen*, 1911, p. 61, Item No. 33.

[40] Joseph Fischer, "Die Carta Marina Waldseemüller's v. Jahre 1516 und die katholischen Missionen," *Katholischen Missionen*, XLV (1917), pp. 13–14; pp. 164–66 contain partial reproductions of the *Carta Marina* of 1525, with a short note on p. 166.

[41] The list of spices and measures is copied literally from the *Newe vnbekanthe Landte* (Nürnberg, 1508), Chapters LXXXII and LXXXIII. The *Newe vnbekanthe Landte* is the German translation by Jobsten Ruchamer of *Paesi Nuovamente Retrovati* (Vicenza, 1507), which is usually ascribed to Fracanzano da Montalboddo (hereafter cited as Ruchamer). Grüninger requested in the letter of June 1, 1524, that Pirckheimer send him "the Capo bona Sperantze. I am making a new *Carta Marina* and want to use it for that," Hase, *Koberger*, "Briefbuch," No. 107. On September 1, he wrote Koberger to remind Pirckheimer, "not to forget to forward [material] for the *Carta Marina*," and on September 17 he wrote to Koberger: "And we send you sir great thanks for the bona sperance," Hase, *Koberger*, "Briefbuch," No. 111, No. 112. The identity of the sentences on the map and the list of spices in Chapter 59 leads us to conclude that Ruchamer's German edition of the *Paesi* was the book which Grüninger requested from Nürnberg. I shall refer to this again (p. 94).

[42] On Waldseemüller's map the distance is not 200 but 260 miles.

[43] Waldseemüller listed more products at this location than Fries: cinnamon, carnelian, carbuncles, hyacinths (iacictes?), sapphires, garnets, topaz, and elephants.

[44] "Pharmacists . . . must pay a lot of money to get the materials from coun-

tries, near and far, for their medicines" (Apotecker . . . müssen auch gross gut daraufflegen, das sy ausz feren vnd nahen landen so mancherley zuwegen bringen), *Spiegel*, 1532, fol. V. Fries found the sentence about the pharmacy in Ruchamer, Chapter LXXXII, footnote 43. Faracola and other weights were also listed on Waldseemüller's map and in Ruchamer.

⁴⁵ Though the legend on the Waldseemüller map can be the source for this, it could also go back to Lodovico de Varthema's *Die Ritterlich vnd lobwirdig rayss des gestrengen vnd über all ander weyt erfarnen ritters vnd Lantfarers herren Ludowico Varthomans* (Augsburg, 1515), in the chapter on Borney (Borneo) fol. p. iii: "In diser ynsel hält man vast gutte gerechtigkayt."

⁴⁶ The legend reads, literally translated: "The realm of Seylan [Ceylon] is divided into four parts. They pray to idols there. There carbuncles and iacictes grow. There is the mountain on which Adam repented."

⁴⁷ This legend does not resemble the inscription by Waldseemüller in the corresponding location; samat may be *samt*, velvet.

⁴⁸ The first edition of Marco Polo's *Travels* was in German (Nürnberg, 1477); it was reprinted in Augsburg in 1481. See Henri Cordier, ed., *The Book of Ser Marco Polo . . .; translated and edited with notes by Colonel Sir Henry Yule*, 3rd ed. (2 vols.; London, 1921), II, pp. 554–82, for a bibliography of editions of this work.

⁴⁹ Waldseemüller was guilty of the same oversight between sheets c and d.

⁵⁰ On Waldseemüller's map of 1516 the symbol for the town in which the Patriarch resided still looked unmistakably German.

⁵¹ The unintelligible German print reads: "Da ist vo k da mntze sich dy ma nit dy wib," which in proper German would read "Da ist Volk, da puzen sich die Männer nicht die Weiber." If it had not been for Waldseemüller's "ornati" it could not have been unraveled.

⁵² The German reads: Hze ist da andmer/da würt mumia fundi/dz i menschenfleisch d' artzni. This is almost comical in terms of contemporary German, even if it was not standardized by 1525. The Latin legend to the left of this about the sea of blackened sand where the mummies were found was rendered in better German. Fries did not include Waldseemüller's remark that the mummies were thought to date back ten or twenty thousand years. The Latin "mistis montibus colligitur de celo manna in magna copia" is not well translated either by "an den bergen felt das hymelbrot in groser zal."

⁵³ Fries called it *Kaufhaus*, department store, and not bazaar.

⁵⁴ Macometangest, which appears along this river directly above the figure of the King of Gambia, was not the name of this river. Waldseemüller had, almost illegibly, mocometanoest, in small carved printing running into the figure of the King of Senegal. He printed no name for the river where Fries repeats Macometangest along the river. Waldseemüller meant, of course, that the region was Mohammedan. This was the Niger River, which was believed to flow from east to west until Mungo Park in 1799 proved otherwise.

[55] This group of seven islands was "Iste insula chamada secusam" on Wald-seemüller's map. The group appears on the Juan de la Cusa map of 1500 and is probably the same Waldseemüller put on the Ptolemy map of 1507 farther south as "insule delle pulz elle." It was believed that the sirens lived there; the group is shown on maps in Charles de la Roncière, *La Découverte de l'Afrique au Moyen Age* (3 vols.; Cairo, 1924–1927), II, pp. 72–73.

[56] Waldseemüller has cidoped, Fries has cirlopedes. I interpret this as cirripeds and assume that the term was as meaningful to lay people as anthrophages and monocli (one-eyed men) were. West Africa is the correct location for the kingdom of Melli; in East Africa another Regnum Melli should be Mellindi, poorly printed on the Waldseemüller map and incorrectly rendered by Fries.

[57] The Cape of Good Hope had numerous spellings in the sixteenth century. In *Den rechten neg auss zu faren von Lissbona gen Kallakuth* ([Nürnberg, ca. 1505]), the Cape is printed as "Kabe de bansprantzsa."

[58] The large unnamed island should have had the name Isabella at that time, but Waldseemüller forgot it and Fries was not one to add place names.

[59] Ruchamer, Chapter CXVI, is the background for the legend about Corterati. The year 1510 should have been 1501.

[60] The "aurochs" (European bison) appears to be the idea behind this drawing. Fries reversed the names of Islanda and Frilland for the two respective islands which Waldseemüller had corrected on his work map to Islanda and Frillanda so that Island would be the northern of the two. For the treatment of the northern regions by Waldseemüller, see Joseph Fischer, *The Discoveries of the Norsemen in America, With Special Relation to Their Early Cartographical Representation*, tr. from the German by Basil H. Soulsby (London and St. Louis, 1903), pp. 82ff.

[61] One example of the long traditions in geographic education which are not yet understood or investigated is the following. In an inexpensive and very service-able edition by Harold Fullard of *Philip's Modern School Atlas*, 55th ed. (Chicago, 1960), sold as *Cartocraft Geography School Atlas*, pp. 68–69, a map with the scale 1:15,000 names every little river and a great number of places on the Guinea coast, with a place-name arrangement similar to the *Carta Marina*'s. The same atlas, pp. 86–87, names two rivers only for the Biloxi coast, and has a different arrangement of place names. This map is on the scale of 1:12,000,000. Thus scale is no explanation for the amazing detail along the West Africa coast. This is in no way a criticism of the atlas.

THE BOOK AND THE MAP

[1] *Uslegung*, introduction, fol. Aii, all three editions; *namhafftigen ding* seems best rendered "renowned place."

[2] A concise description of the development of the names and numbers of winds can be found in Brown, *Story of Maps*, pp. 123–26. Fries's list of winds in the book corresponds exactly to the names on the frames, but interestingly, does not

Notes

run consecutively around the wind rose but is arranged as follows: upper frame from left to right, left frame from top to bottom, bottom frame from left to right, right frame from top to bottom.

[3] The typesetters' errors notwithstanding, it seems certain that Fries regularly called mariners "Marinal"; he contrasts *weithe des meres* with *einer enge als in telern oder vff den Bergen* (*Uslegung*, 1525, fol. Aii verso) translated "with narrows, valleys, and hills." The Vosges Mountains and not the Alps are brought to mind by his vocabulary.

[4] Compare pp. 35–36, where the *Spiegel* is discussed.

[5] *Uslegung*, Chapter 3, all three editions; *als weit als dan sich zum höchsten mügliche wonung der menschen volstreket*.

[6] It reads in heading III "und so offt sich der lengst tag umb ein halbe stund ufferhept so setzen sie ein underschied eins Climats" ("and as often as the longest day gets to be half an hour longer a different climate begins"). A comparison of the difference between Fries's explanation and more careful computations such as those by Pierre d'Ailly helps to understand the "popular level" at which Fries presented this somewhat abstruse topic. Compare Edmond Buron, *Pierre d'Ailly, Imago Mundi* (3 vols.; Paris, 1930), I, pp. 159, 161. For information about the Greek origin and Strabo's presentation of primary zones, climates, and the habitable world, see Chapter II in Brown, *Story of Maps*.

[7] The arrangement of chapters, detailed description, and vocabulary make it most unlikely that Fries used Waldseemüller's *Cosmographiae Introductio* at all. This would also explain why the latter's explanation of the crosses around islands escaped him. It is found on the verso of the folded global diagram. "Ed quod nõ est ignorandum vadosa maris littora (ubi naufragia timentur) imaginibus crucis signauimus . . ."

[8] Examples of the awkwardness with which the letters carved in gothic minuscule were scattered are "russia alba" close to the upper border of sheet c, "macini-regio" on both sides of the mountain crest in eastern India, "narsinga" north and south of the equator in India, "Arabia foelix" on the Arabian peninsula.

[9] Grüninger to Hans Koberger, February 23, 1524, in Hase, *Koberger*, "Briefbuch," No. 106.

[10] One German mile of the period equals roughly 7.42 kilometers. The distance between Basel and Strassburg was about 15.2 such miles because there is a bend in the road which leads via Mülhausen and Colmar to Strassburg. The wording of the instructions in the *Uslegung* is very similar to that of Erhard Etzlaub's instructions on his late-fifteenth-century map of Central Europe. It is likely that Fries saw Etzlaub's map or that Waldseemüller, who is known to have used it, left a note which Fries used. See the collation by W. Ruge, *Nachrichten von der . . . Gesellschaft . . . zu Göttingen*, 1904, p. 19.

[11] The awareness of the significance of navigable waterways is impressively reflected in Hieronymus Gebwiler's *Strassburger Chronik*, Chapter IV. See the excellent investigation by Karl Stenzel, tr. and ed., "Die Strassburger Chronik

des elsässischen Humanisten Hieronymus Gebwiler," *Schriften des Wissenschaft-lichen Instituts der Elsass-Lothringer i.R. an der Universität Frankfurt a.M.*, [X] (1926), p. 43. For the problem of the traditionally wrong bend of the Rhine on maps of the first decades of the sixteenth century, which Sebastian Münster finally corrected, see Wolkenhauer, *Abhandlungen der . . . Gesellschaft . . . zu Göttingen*, XI, No. 3, pp. 54–65.

[12] *Uslegung*, Chapter 92, 1525 edition; shortened in 1527 and omitted in 1530. The Order of the Knights Hospitalers of St. John had taken the city of Rhodes in 1310; in 1522 they lost it to the Turks, who held it until 1912.

[13] It could be, however, that Fries mistook the group of islands "Iste insule chamada secusam" for the Canary Islands. The island group by this same name in addition to an island called y thebas based upon Waldseemüller's .y. tebas is located according to Waldseemüller's grid at latitude 9–10 degrees south and longitude 6–9 degrees east counting from a prime meridian at the island of Porto Sancto. The only earlier map to show islands with these names is Juan de la Cusa's map of 1500, see note 55, p. 142.

[14] There was as yet no standard German, and it was spoken in many dialects and varied greatly in printing. An example of the variation in the spelling of place names is Melinde, spelled ten different ways in Franz Schulze, ed., *Balthasar Springers Indienfahrt 1505/06* (Strassburg, 1902), p. 20.

[15] The Latin edition is mentioned by Bagrow, *Catalogus*, No. 199, p. 73: "Im Jahre 1530 erschien auch eine freie Übertragung ins Lateinische von Nicolaus Prugner: *Hydrographiae, hoc est chartae marinae totiusque orbis, breuis sed dilucida descriptio*. Argentorati Joannes Gruningerus excudebat anno MDXXX. 4°, 16 Bl., mit einem kleinen Globus auf dem Titelblatte." There is no further reference. It is possible that Bagrow's knowledge came from Henry Harrisse, *The Discovery of North America* (London and Paris, 1892), p. 578, No. 191, where it is described as "an extremely rare tract," and a translation or paraphrase of Lorenz Fries's *Carta Marina* written by Nicolaus Prugner. Prugner, formerly a pastor at Mülhausen, lived at Benfeld, about seventeen miles south of Strassburg, around 1530 and was deeply interested in astrology, astronomy, and mathematics. No copy of Prugner's abbreviated Latin version of the *Uslegung* is extant. For biographical data and details about Prugner see Ritter, *Histoire de l'Imprimerie*, p. 523; Jules Lutz, "Les Réformateurs de Mulhouse: Nicolas Prugner," Bulletin du Musée Historique de Mulhouse, XXVI (1902), pp. 32–68; XXVII (1903), pp. 10–68; XXXV (1911), pp. 35–60; XXXVI (1912), pp. 31–51; Philippe Mieg, "Quelques détails nouveaus sur Nicolas Prugner, Réformateur de Mulhouse," *ibid.*, XLIX (1929), pp. 47–57.

[16] The following places are in the register without numbers: Bern (Switzerland), Baden ("oben," in Switzerland), Baden ("Margraf," in the Black Forest), Breysach, Colmar, Canstatt, Einsyden, Esslingen, Eystat, Friburg in Uchtland, Farrer, Grienyngen, Hagenau, Heilbronn, Ingolstatt, Keysersberg, Königshoffen, Landshut, Mühlhausen, Mantua, Rothenburg am Neckar, Solothurn, Schaffhausen,

Notes

Schlettstadt, Tübingen, Tolosa (Toulouse), Überlingen, Weissenburg, Würzburg, Zürich.

[17] These non-European cities were Alexandria, Calicut, Constantinople, Cairo, Damascus, Heliopolis, Medina, Mecca, Pego (in India), Rodos, Taurisium.

[18] These twenty-one place names here associated with the age of discovery, are America, Cape of Good Hope, Cape Verde, India, Fesa, Guzerath, Cannibals' Island, Canary Islands, Java, Madeira, Melli, Murfuli, Narsinga, Orchades Islands in the north, the islands of Ormuz, Prasilia, Spagnola, Samotra, Senegal, Cuba, Zeyla. Several were known earlier, but they continue to be frequently mentioned in travel literature of the time. Such classification is necessarily somewhat arbitrary.

[19] The names of these towns were Asperg, Büteldorff, Burghusen, Kemten, Koblentz, Nümeg, Vincentz, Vilach, Vlmnitz (Olmnitz), Wiltbad, Vitenburg, Wissmar, Waiblingen.

[20] This map may have been part of an originally larger map, since the right margin appears to have been cut off. The Ruchamer translation calls the island Monchritus, or Monchrico in the fifth chapter. Fries did not draw this map. It must have been a map which Waldseemüller designed with additional detail in place names and on a larger scale, although it was called a "map of a part of the Atlantic Ocean by Laur. Frisius, 1525." It is reproduced in A. E. Nordenskiöld, *Periplus* (Stockholm, 1897), p. 119, and is the same as that in the 1525 edition of the *Uslegung*. Henry Harrisse, *Discovery of North America*, p. 539, mentions this map with the same title; but the German inscription in the inset is different, and since Harrisse also mentions that "Terra de Cuba Partis Africe" and a translation of Oceanus occidentalis as "Das mer gegen nidergang" were on the map he saw, it is obvious that he saw a different map. We can be certain, therefore, that it was issued in two versions, and the advertisement on it of a larger book makes it highly probable that it was also distributed separately. This is the second time that we have found a map in a book by Grüninger which could have been issued separately, the first being the Terre Novae sheet in the 1522 Ptolemy.

[21] The passage in the *Uslegung* of 1525 reads: "hie nit ein Cronik beschreiben wollen"; in 1527: "hier nit ein Cronica beschreiben wöllen"; in 1530: "hye nit ein Cronica Beschrybenn wöllen." References to "another" or "a bigger" book are frequent in the *Uslegung*, though varying from one edition to another.

[22] Grüninger to Pirckheimer, undated (late April 1525) in Hase, *Koberger,* "Briefbuch," No. 123.

[23] In the city library at Nürnberg there is a manuscript copy of Newe zeittung von dem lande das die Sponier funden haben ym 1521, iare genant Jucatan., dated March 19, 1522, and by Pirckheimer, according to Walther Ruge, "Aelteres kartographisches Material in deutschen Bibliotheken." *Nachrichten von der Königlichen Gesellschaft der Wissenschaften zu Göttingen. Philologisch-historische Klasse* (1916, Beiheft), pp. 59, 98.

[24] For Ringmann's share and further details of this preparatory work see M. C.

Schmidt, "Mathias Ringmann (Philesius) Humaniste Alsacien et Lorrain," *Mémoires de la Societé d'Archéologie Lorraine*, 3rd series, Vol. III, Part 2 (1875), pp. 165–233; particularly pp. 210–12.

[25] Ptolemy, 1522, Tabula Moderna Germaniae: "vt qui Vualdensium sectã amplexi tutentur, tum aurorum nostrorum memoria Hussitarum veneno infecti." Tabula Moderna Bossinae, Serviae, Gretiae et Sclavoniae: "In hac Athene ciuitas liberalium litterarum et philosophorum mater."

[26] The last six lines of the text in the Ptolemy of 1522 for Tabula Terre Sancte foreshadow this stronger criticism of Judea in the *Uslegung* in the chapters on Judea of 1525, 1527, and 1530, which are alike except for differences in spelling.

[27] *Uslegung*, 1525 and 1527, "Von der insul Engelland," Chapter 2; omitted in the 1530 edition.

[28] Schmidt, *Grüninger*, item No. 191: *Ob der Künig usz engelland ein lügner sey oder der Luther* (Strassburg, 1522).

[29] *Uslegung*, "Von Lipsigk," Chapter 53 in 1525, Chapter 69 in 1527, Chapter 65 in 1530.

[30] *Uslegung*, "Von Nubia" Chapter 66 in 1525, Chapter 78 in 1527, abbreviated in Chapter 78 in 1530. The reference to Christians is in all three editions. The passage after "Nubia, a land and kingdom near the true moors' land" begins with "Das volk in diser Insul ist Christen." It is not clear why this land should be called an island. However, the reference to Christians, "doch garbey uff den Lutherschen schlag," corresponds with the map legend on the *Carta Marina* which tells about the Jacobites.

[31] *Uslegung*, "Von Poland," Chapter 63 in 1525; Chapter 85 in 1527, Chapter 85 in 1530. The short paragraph on Cracow in all three editions does not contain any reference to religion.

[32] *Uslegung*, "Von Taurisio," Chapter 106 in 1525; Chapter 111 in 1527; Chapter 104 in 1530. "Von der Walachi," Chapter 112 in 1525; Chapter 117 in 1527; Chapter 115 in 1530. The identical passage reads "Ir glaub ist wie der kriechischen sect."

[33] This same reference is found in all three editions in the short unnumbered passage following the nine chapters of the introductory part.

[34] *Uslegung*, all three editions, chapter about cannibals: "und haben ein insul innen/ welche Christoffel dauber von Janua bei kurtzen iaren erfunden hat." (Italics mine.)

[35] This passage in *Uslegung*, 1525 edition, fol. B, is not in the 1527 and 1530 editions, where the longer second part of this chapter is omitted. (Italics mine.)

[36] This is neither Waldseemüller's nor Fries's original report, but is taken from Chapter XI in Ruchamer's *Newe vnbekanthe Landte*. The passage about medicine in *Uslegung*, Chapter 75, "Meli," was considerably abbreviated in 1530.

[37] Thaddäus Florentinus of the thirteenth century, who was called a second Hippocrates and Galenus, died around 1300. He is reported to have cured Pope Honorius IV, and was the author of seven books listed in Zedler, *Universal-*

Notes

Lexikon, XLIII, pp. 334–335. His last work, *Comment in Avicennae opera*, dealt with Avicenna, the same medical authority who was praised by Fries in his last work, *Defensio Medicorum Principis Avicennae, ad Germaniae Medicos*.

[38] This does not even take into consideration that Fries, who abbreviated many chapters from Ruchamer's translation, left out several passages which refer to medicine; compare, for instance, the chapter on Senegal in Ruchamer, *Newe vnbekanthe Landte*, Chapter XV, and in the 1525 *Uslegung*, Chapter 110.

[39] *Spiegel*, 1532, fol. xxxiii.

[40] Fries quotes the names of the classical scholars in too general a fashion to justify a search for specific derivations. Konrad Celtis wrote *Norimbergia* in 1495. The book was published in 1502, in a collective volume which also contained *Amores, Ludus Dianae*, and a "sample description" of Germany. See Hans Rupprich, "Der Briefwechsel des Konrad Celtis," in *Veröffentlichungen der Kommission zur Erforschung der Geschichte der Reformation und Gegenreformation, Humanistenbriefe* (5 vols.; Munich, 1934), III, p. xvii. Fries praised Hieronymus in 1518 in the introduction to the *Spiegel*. Froben's publication between 1516 and 1520, of Hieronymus' works in Greek under the editorship of Erasmus was a great scholarly event of which every educated person was aware. Compare Knapp, *Deutscher Buchhandel*, pp. 389–92. Fries excerpted long passages for his chapters on Madeira, the Canary Islands, Calicut, the Cape of Good Hope, Senegal, and Melli from Ruchamer. For Mecca, Medina, Narsinga, and Pego, Fries copied from Varthema's *Die Ritterlich vnd lobwirdig rayss*. The first chapter of the second part of the *Uslegung* about Amerigo Vespucci was taken from *Disz büchlin saget . . .* (Strassburg: Grüninger, 1509), a German translation of the "Quatuor Navigationes" of Vespucci first published in the *Cosmographia Introductio* by Waldseemüller. There are no identifiable details from Mandeville in the *Uslegung*. Eleven German editions of his fabulous reports had appeared by 1507, six between 1483 and 1507 in Strassburg, according to Paul Heitz and François Ritter, *Versuch einer Zusammenstellung der Deutschen Volksbücher des 15. und 16. Jahrhunderts* (Strassburg, 1924), pp. 114–15.

[41] *Uslegung*, "Beschlussred," in all three editions. Let us recall that Fries called Grüninger a "truly honest man" in his preface of 1530 to the *Spiegel* and said he was not to be blamed for the mistakes of typesetters; this is also the year that this request for Grüninger's protection was printed for the last time.

[42] Only the initial "W" for Wien and Walachia is the same gothic capital letter as in the text of 1525.

[43] More than twenty-five different type faces have been recognized in Grüninger's publications; see Ernst Voullième, *Die Deutschen Drucker des Fünfzehnten Jahrhunderts*, 2nd ed. (Berlin, 1922), p. 154. The term "Upper Rhine German letter type" is a translation of "oberrheinische deutsche Schrift" as it is discussed in Preussische Staatsbibliothek, *Deutscher Buchdruck im Jahrhundert Gutenbergs* (Leipzig, 1940), Tafel, 580. Paul H. Heitz, in a letter of March 2, 1962, answered my question regarding the proper classification of the type used in the

Uslegung with "minuscule, gothique avec influence française." He also suggested "un terme amusant," namely, "de la rue de l'outre," that is, gothic minuscule with French influence or in *Schlauchgasse* style.

⁴⁴ One example is the text for the country of Barbaria. Fries defended it, saying that it really did not have an uncouth language and was called *pürisch* (*bäurisch* = rustic) only by the Greeks, who he said called everything not Greek barbaric. They even called a German Meistersinger a barbarian or a big "Kochersperger." The edition of 1530 has the same text throughout except that Kochersperger is now Bayer, i.e., Bavarian. The reflection of Fries's anti-Greek attitude in this passage is corroborated by other of his statements, but there is no reason to investigate the altered insult.

⁴⁵ *Uslegung*, "Von Italia" in 1525 and 1527, last three sentences left out in 1530. "Both laws" means Roman and canonical law. *Pactry*, pactmanship, is rendered as statesmanship. Theology is *göttliche Geschrifft*. "Equally . . . administration of justice" reads in Fries: "Dessgleichen wil man haben betrachtung gemeins nutz und handhabung der gerechtigkeit."

⁴⁶ *Pürisch* or *bäurisch* is a stereotype often combined with *grob*, translated rustic and uncouth.

⁴⁷ *Uslegung*, "Von Litua," 1525 and 1527. In 1530 an almost incomprehensible sentence was added: "Also various leather sold for Egern currency [*Batzen* = an old coin] and impure sheep tallow mixed with grit."

⁴⁸ *Uslegung*, "Von Orchades," the same in all three editions.

⁴⁹ Frankfurt was the only town in southern Germany in 1525 which had not expelled the Jews and forced them to live outside its walls. The passage about the Jews in Frankfurt was left out in 1530.

⁵⁰ This would be about thirty-two statute miles. The lake is forty-two miles long.

⁵¹ *Uslegung*, "Von Rome," 1525. In 1527 and 1530 the chapter closed thus: "Read all you can about all the cities in the world it has it all in abundance." Fries called Rome's port of Ostia *Hostiam*. The Tiber flows through Rome in a general northeast–southwest direction.

⁵² The treatment of Lisbon (Lisbona), 26 lines, remained unabridged throughout the three editions. For Antwerp (Antdorff), 21 lines, the promise that "more will be told in the other book" was left out in 1530. Approximately a third of the chapter about Venice, describing the canals, 29 lines, was no longer printed in 1530.

⁵³ In the 1530 edition the chapters describing Alexandria, Mecca, and Medina were reduced, whereas the descriptions of Constantinople, Cairo, Heliopolis, and Damascus kept their original length.

⁵⁴ *Uslegung*, "Von Turtia," differs in 1525 and 1530 and was shortened in the second by about a third. The reference to a Jewess who trained Mohammed was left out. The statement "that the Jews were wrong to deny Christ's birth by a virgin" was changed to "consider it erroneous that Christians believe in the son

of God and Mary." The last sentence of 1525 to the effect that "the emperor let everyone have his own faith" was left out in 1530.

⁵⁵ The imperial double-headed eagle with a crown is now accepted as by Hans Baldung Grien. It appeared for the first time on the title page of *Ordnung und besonderes Gesetz des heiligen römischen Reichs Hofgericht zu Rottweil* (Strassburg: Grüninger, 1523). One of the shields the eagle holds in its claws is the coat of arms of a count, the other is not identified. Both shields were taken out and as "edition b" the figure was reused not only for the second edition of the *Uslegung* but also in a publication by Grüninger's son in 1536. See Kunsthalle Karlsruhe, *Grien*, pp. 384–85.

⁵⁶ This report is based upon Varthema's travels, but Fries replaced Varthema's comparison of Narsinga's countryside with Naples and Venice by a comparison of Narsinga with Naples and Calabria. Both compare the city of Narsinga with Milan.

⁵⁷ For reference to the Fondaco which Titian and Giorgione decorated see Willy Andreas, *Deutschland vor der Reformation*, 2nd ed. (Stuttgart and Berlin, 1934), p. 313. The technique of showing cities as seen from the water — ocean or river — was typical and whenever possible used for cities in Hartmann Schedel's *Registrum Huius Operis Libri Cronicorum cum Figuris et Ymagibus ab Inicio Mundi* (Nürnberg, 1493).

⁵⁸ Grüninger wrote to Hans Koberger on August 13, 1524, that he was still hoping for "lissbona die stat und beschreibung," Hase, *Koberger*, "Briefbuch," No. 110.

⁵⁹ The desire of Waldseemüller to retract the name "America" has been emphasized more than the fact that contradictory ambiguities persisted for some time. See Konrad Kretschmer, *Die Entdeckung Amerika's in ihrer Bedeutung für die Geschichte des Weltbildes* (Berlin, 1892), pp. 365–66.

⁶⁰ *Carta Marina*, cased legend directly above small shield along left margin.

⁶¹ Münster mentioned Fries as one of the scholars whose works he used (see Friedrich S. Vögelin, "Sebastian Münster's Cosmographey," *Basler Jahrbuch*, 1882, p. 130) after he invited Fries among other scholars to cooperate with him in a work to be called *Cosmographia*, according to his preface to *Erklerung des newen Instruments der Sunnen* (Oppenheim, 1528). It is quite possible that Grüninger, according to his letter to Hans Koberger, February 23, 1524, meant to enlist Münster's services also for the second edition of his Ptolemy (see Hase, *Koberger*, "Briefbuch," No. 106 and Wolkenhauer, "*Abhandlungen der . . . Gesellschaft . . . zu Göttingen*, XI, No. 3, pp. 21–24, 36). Both Fries and Münster copied and used Waldseemüller's maps extensively.

⁶² For a similar evaluation see Joachim Lelewel, *Géographie du Moyen Age* (5 vols.; Brussels, 1852–1857), II, pp. 124–25, where he speaks of 40 editions of Ptolemy in less than a hundred years.

⁶³ An excellent reproduction of one of the Ptolemy manuscripts from which translators had to work is Victor Langlois, *Géographie de Ptolémée, Reproduc-*

tion Photolithographique du Manuscrit Grec du Monastère de Valopédi au Mont Athos (Paris, 1867).

[64] A good example of another such map on which similar framed legends, pavilions, kings, animals, and riders appear is A. Jenkinson's map of Russia from A. Ortelius' *Theatrum Orbis Terrarum* (Antwerp, 1570), discussed by Johann Keuning, "Jenkinson's Map of Russia," *Imago Mundi*, XIII (The Hague, 1956), p. 173.

[65] David Lowenthal, "Geography, Experience and Imagination: Towards a Geographical Epistemology," *Annals of the Association of American Geographers*, LI (1961), p. 246. The quotation is from Loren C. Eiseley, *The Firmament of Time*, New York, 1960, p. 38.

INDEX

Index

Fries, Lorenz: 3, 4, 5, 10, 29, 73, 75, 81, 114, 116; on Strassburg, 5; first book for Grüninger, 24; birthplace, 33–34; on syphilis, 34; in Strassburg, 35; *Spiegel der Artzney*, 35–36; and Murner, 38; *Ein kurtze Shirmred der Kunst Astrologie*, 38; prognostications, 38; edits Ptolemy, *1522*, 41–44; *Expositio Ususque Astrolabii*, 45; *Der Juden Practica*, 45; leaves Strassburg, 46; last years and death, 47; his *Carta Marina* compared with other maps, 53, 54, 55, 59, 61–62, 63, 64, 65, 67, 70, 71; and Waldseemüller's material, 59, 96, 97, 98, 99; and *Carta Marina, 1516*, 59–63; as a copyist, 70; use of symbols, 71; lacks missionary spirit, 74; acknowledgment of Waldseemüller, 85; on wind rose, 85–87; on climates, 87–89; map technique, 89; anti-Lutheranism, 97; on Holy Land, 97; on European countries in *Uslegung*, 101–103; on Jews in Frankfurt, 104; on European cities in *Uslegung*, 104, 105–106

Friesland, 34

Froben, Johann, 26

Galen, 35

Gallia, 43

Gallic disease, 11, 34, 111

Gambia, 68, 80

Ganges, 78

Gebwiler, Hieronymus, 19, 25, 46

Geiler von Kaysersberg, Johann, 11, 12

Gengenbach, Pamphilius, 38, 39

Genoa (Janus), 102, 103, 105

Gibraltar, 61–62

Giovanni de Plano Carpini, 74

Glockendon, George, illustrator in Nürnberg, 68

Globus Mundi Declaratio sive Descriptio Mundi, 23

Gothic minuscule, 66, 100, 101

Great Lutheran Fool (1522), 25

Greece, Fries on, 33, 96, 102

grid: 59; on *Carta Marina 1516*, 55, 57

Grien, Hans Baldung, designer for Grüninger, 19, 20, 35, 66, 107

Grüninger, Johannes: 4, 9, 10, 34, 35, 37, 41, 43, 47, 55, 73, 114; and *Uslegung*, 3; bookstalls of, 5; modes of shipping books, 7; office, 11; printer of sermons, 12; plans to leave Strassburg, 13; biography, 17; first period, *1484–1502*, 18–20; illustrators employed by, 19–20; second period, *1503–1517*, 20–23; and copyright, 20, 64; and Waldseemüller's material, 21–24, 39, 57; and *Instructio Manuductionem Pretans in Cartem Itinerariam, 1511, 1520, 1527*, 23; and religion, 24–26, 39; third period, *1517–1531*, 24–29; as decorator of maps, 27, 44, 61, 67, 68; and Koberger, 28; and Pirckheimer, 25–27, 28, 57; and Fries, 37; Ptolemy of *1522*, 41, 44; Ptolemy of *1525*, 26, 27, 45; *Carta Marina*, 46, 53; dedication in *Uslegung*, 85; requests for material about foreign places, 94; *Chronica Mundi* project, 95, 96; illustrations in *Uslegung*, 107–113; wall maps, 116

guayac wood, 34, 40, 98, 99

Guinea coast, 71, 80

Gutenberg, Johann, 5, 11

Hagenau, 46

Hamaharic (Abyssinia), 79

Hedio, Caspar, of Ettlingen, 12

Heitz (publishing house), 47

Heliopolis, 106

Hellas, 33

Hellespont, 88

Hesperides, 73

Hieronymus, 100

Hippocrates, 35, 38

Index

THIS *book, in Linotype Times Roman on Mohawk Superfine Text, was designed by Jane McCarthy of the University of Minnesota Press. It was composed and printed at the Lund Press, Minneapolis and bound at the National Bookbinding Company Stevens Point, Wisconsin. Of the limited edition of 750 copies this is copy*

143